**Excerpts from two of the stories:**

**From "The Sinister Evil of the Black Death"** . . .

The dreaded disease took hold almost immediately. No one knows for sure, but some reports claimed that the disease nearly wiped out the entire city—tens of thousands of people died. In desperation, ship owners and sailors sailed away, hoping to escape death. But the disease sailed with them. And then it spread across Europe.

**From "The Fury of Rabies"** . . .

The bats drifted soundlessly through open windows. They landed lightly on their victims. For unknown reasons, the bats seemed particularly drawn to children. Perhaps it was because the children's hearts beat faster. The vampire bats used their sensitive noses to detect bare skin. Creeping along blankets, they found exposed arms, necks, and faces. The bats sunk their teeth into the children. Then, they lapped up blood for nearly 30 minutes. Not one child woke up.

MARIE NOBLE

TP THE TOWNSEND LIBRARY

# SCARY MEDICAL STORIES

TP THE TOWNSEND LIBRARY

For more titles in the Townsend Library,
visit our website: **www.townsendpress.com**


Printed in the United States of America

9 8 7 6 5 4 3 2 1



**Townsend Press, Inc.**
**439 Kelley Drive**
**West Berlin, NJ 08091**
**permissions@townsendpress.com**

ISBN-13: 978-1-59194-292-4
ISBN-10: 1-59194-292-6

Library of Congress Control Number:
2012932250

# CONTENTS

# INTRODUCTION

The human body is almost too amazing to be believed.

Consider these facts: Our heart beats around 100,000 times a day, continuously pumping blood through 60,000 miles of blood vessels. And we take more than 25,000 breaths a day. We do all this without even thinking about it. When we touch something, information about what we've touched races to our brain at about 240 miles an hour. And our brain holds five times more information than an entire set of encyclopedias. Our eyes can recognize close to one million different colors and shapes. A sneeze rockets dust out of our nose at nearly 100 miles an hour.

Perhaps one of the most astounding things about the body is that it can repair itself. Except for our teeth, every bit of our body is living, growing tissue. More than 2 trillion new cells are formed in our body every day. So if we're healthy, tissue can heal and rebuild itself when it's broken or torn.

The human body works nonstop to stay healthy. Even when we mistreat or overwork our body, it does everything it can to stay well. What if we drink or eat things that are unhealthy? First, the kidneys clean our blood with millions of tiny filters. Then the liver works to flush the collected wastes out of our body. What if we push our body too hard during a workout? Overused muscles get extra protein rushed to them so that they can rebuild. And when we stay up too late, our body eventually forces us to sleep—whether we want to or not.

As miraculous and hardworking as the body is, sometimes it gets overwhelmed. This can happen when a person abuses drugs, alcohol, or unhealthy food. Too much of a bad thing always takes its toll. Then the body revolts by giving up and shutting down. Our body is most likely to reach the breaking point when germs are attacking it. When our body cannot combat that attack, we get sick.

Amazingly, only 150 years ago, no one even knew what a germ was. Most people still believed that illness was caused by evil spirits or foul-smelling air or even too much blood in the body. However, Louis Pasteur, working in France, and Robert Koch, working in Germany, had other ideas. In 1865, while examining the remains of some sour beer under his microscope, Pasteur observed thousands of little dots swimming around. Those wiggly dots were actually bacteria. Pasteur wondered if the bacteria could be the reason the beer had spoiled.

Pasteur and Koch also wondered if bacteria could make people sick. After all, people sometimes got sick when they drank spoiled milk or beer. Pasteur developed a theory: He believed that bacteria floated in the air, and if they landed in beer (or any other drink that could spoil), they could ruin it. Furthermore, he believed that these same tiny dots could drift through the air unseen, invade human beings, and make them ill. Pasteur called this his "germ theory."

Many scientists and doctors thought Pasteur was crazy.

"I'm afraid these experiments will turn against you," one doctor warned Pasteur. "The world into which you wish to take us is really too unbelievable."

This new "world" of germs was, indeed, both hard to believe and frightening. Illnesses could float unseen through the air? Impossible! Tiny bacteria could sneak into a grown man and make him deathly ill? Ridiculous! But in time, scientists and doctors would come to see that Pasteur was right. Disease did not begin on its own inside the human body—it began when a germ entered the body.

So what exactly are germs?

One kind of germ, as Pasteur noticed, is bacteria. Bacteria are living things made of only one cell. They are so small that they can be seen only with a microscope. Bacteria can be found everywhere. Most bacteria are completely harmless. In fact, our own skin is literally covered with millions of bacteria. When bacteria get inside us, our body tries to fight them off. However, the bacteria cells can multiply very rapidly. The fight itself may make us sick. Or the bacteria may carry poisons that are released in the course of the fight, making us even sicker. Common diseases that come from bacteria include pneumonia, strep throat, food poisoning, and typhoid.

Another kind of germ is a tiny animal-like creature called a "protozoan." Like bacteria, protozoa have only one cell and can be seen only with a microscope. Protozoa can enter our bloodstream when an infected mosquito or other insect bites us. Saliva from the insect mixes with our blood, and protozoa stream into our body. Under a microscope, these little creatures look something like oval worms that wriggle and swim. Protozoa are responsible for malaria, sleeping sickness, Lyme disease, and many other illnesses.

The tiniest germ may also be the most frightening germ: It is known as a "virus." Unlike bacteria or protozoa, viruses are not alive. They are basically little chemical packages. A virus attaches to a living cell in the body and within that cell creates new virus germs. Then these new germs take over more and more cells, faster and faster. Finally, the virus takes over the entire body and makes the person sick. Some viruses can cause fairly harmless diseases, like the common cold. Other viruses are responsible for some very dangerous illnesses: AIDS, yellow fever, rabies, and flu.

Luckily, our body is prepared to fight germs. The first line of defense is our skin. Unless skin is broken by a cut, germs cannot get through flesh. However, germs tend to like to collect on our hands and beneath our nails. Then when our hands touch our mouth, eyes, or even nose, these germs find their way into our body. (There's a reason why we're always told to wash our hands!) Other times, germs get inside us through insect or animal bites. And, as Pasteur discovered, some germs simply float through the air. Often, this happens when someone sneezes or coughs and doesn't cover his or her mouth. If we take a breath near the sneezer, the germs come into our body.

Once germs have found their way inside, a kind of alarm goes off. Special cells are alerted to the fact that something dangerous has entered our body. These cells rush to the germs and begin eating them. Other alarms go off, and different cells work to figure out how to keep the germs from hurting us. Altogether, this process of cells working together to keep us healthy is known as "immunity."

Sometimes, however, our immunity fails. This happens either because our body is run down or because the attacking germs are too powerful for our immune system to fight. Bit by bit, the infection spreads. That invisible germ you picked up on your pinkie has now become a disease inside your body. Some infections—if they are not treated—can lead to death, perhaps in a very short time.

In this book, you will read true stories about people who have battled terrible diseases. Some will win the battle, and some will not. The first half of the book presents epidemics: the Black Death, smallpox, yellow fever, polio, and AIDS. Disease has always been around, but epidemics have not. Only when people began living together in large communities, about 5,000 years ago, did epidemics begin appearing. An epidemic, after all, is defined as an illness that spreads quickly throughout communities or cities. When humans lived only in small, scattered groups, epidemics were not possible.

How do we know people suffered from epidemics thousands of years ago? Ancient paintings and sculpture show people who appear to be sick with smallpox and polio. Writings describe terrifying "curses" from the gods that caused the death of entire communities. The remains of mummies show signs of certain diseases on the dried skin. Ancient drawings and doctors' notes have helped modern scientists conclude that the illness that wiped out a third of the population of Athens, Greece, around 430 B.C. was most likely typhoid fever. And even in the Bible's Old Testament, ten plagues (an older term for epidemics) are described. These plagues may or may not have happened. But we know from the descriptions that people thousands of years ago were at least familiar with epidemics.

The second half of this book presents other kinds of diseases and illnesses. Some of the diseases, like rabies, may suddenly become more common in certain regions. However, because these diseases don't spread quickly from person to person or wipe out communities, they are not considered epidemics. When they occur in large numbers, they are known as "outbreaks."

Only a few generations ago, epidemics and outbreaks often killed, crippled, or badly sickened millions of people. But, as you will discover in the following stories, modern medicine has helped to change that.

And it's amazing when you think about it.

Disease has been around for many thousands of years. But the understanding of disease has been around for barely 150 years. Incredible advances have been made in a very short time. For example, in the early 1800s, some doctors still believed that drilling holes in the head could relieve headaches. Only 200 years later, doctors perform complex brain scans to pinpoint pain.

Still, there are a lot of mysteries. Many things about the human body still stump scientists and doctors. How does the brain really work? How do we store memories? How are emotions created? Why do brains sleep and dream? Answers to these questions could uncover important clues that could help doctors understand many confusing diseases.

Because there is always more to learn, medical research never ends. As advanced as medicine has become in a very short time, disease has still not been conquered. We may seldom see "old" diseases like leprosy, typhoid, tuberculosis, or malaria in the United States. But that doesn't mean that these illnesses aren't raging in other parts of our planet. Countries that are more developed may have drugs to prevent or cure these illnesses, but the illnesses still exist. In fact, only one disease on earth—smallpox—has ever been completely destroyed.

In addition, strange and new diseases appear every year. Sometimes, old diseases are no longer cured by the drugs that once worked. The disease may grow more powerful than the drug. When this happens, an old bug becomes what's known as a "superbug." This is a dangerous new kind of disease that can't be stopped. As recently as March 2011, a new superbug was reported to have spread across the entire United States. Even though cases of these superbugs are rare, they're still fairly frightening.

"It sounds like something out of a scary movie, but it's real," a Los Angeles health official commented. "It's a grim, but important, reminder. Science and medicine may have raced forward to catch up with disease. But disease is still ahead."

CHAPTER 1

## The Sinister Evil of the Black Death

It was a morning like any other morning in the harbor town of Messina, Sicily, just south of Italy. Perhaps it was a bit warm for late October, but no one minded. For years, the weather had been cold and rainy. Crops had died, and people had starved by the thousands throughout Europe. This year, however, the sun had shone more often than not, and the fields were full of grain. Finally, it seemed, life was getting back to normal.

"Attention!" people shouted from the docks. "Ships are coming in!"

Moving slowly into the harbor were twelve Italian ships. The year was 1347, and Italians had only recently begun trading with merchants in eastern Asia. It was a long journey to Asia, but it was a journey worth taking. Exotic spices, silks, and jewels fascinated Europeans, and they were willing to pay a lot of money for those items.

Now, as the ships drew closer, dockworkers could see the colorful flags that indicated that this fleet was indeed returning from Asia. Excitement grew, and townspeople began gathering near the docks. Children shouted, and jumped up and down. Sometimes the sailors had strange creatures and brightly colored birds with them when they came ashore. Everyone wanted the best view of the ships and the hundreds of sailors who would be lining the decks and waving as they anchored.

But something was wrong.

"Where is everyone?" a young boy whispered to his mother.

Suddenly, a hush fell over the docks. Only one or two men could be seen on the deck of each ship. In fact, one ship appeared to have no one at all on board as it sailed dangerously close to the ship in front of it. As the ships drew close to the docks, a gasp rippled through the crowd. The faces of the few sailors on deck were ghostly white. Huge black lumps grew on their necks, and many of them had blood and pus covering their clothing. One sailor was entirely covered in oozing red sores.

"Quickly!" mothers called to their children. "Don't let the sailors get near you!"

Many of the sailors had died on the journey from Asia, but now the men who had survived stumbled from the ships in agony. Some collapsed, crying out for help. Others staggered toward the crowd, but the crowd shrank back in horror. The dockworkers whispered nervously to one another. They had never seen anything like this before. What was it? What should they do? Finally, the workers shouted to the sailors to return to their ships.

"You may dock here tonight, but you must stay on board your ships. In the morning, you must leave Messina."

The people of Messina thought they would be safe from this terrible disease. After all, the sailors never even entered the town, and nobody got near them. That night, the only "cargo" that left the ships was the black rats that ran down the dock ropes and into Messina looking for food. In the morning, the ghostly ships sailed soundlessly away into the fog.

In less than a week, however, dozens of dockworkers began feeling a strange chill. Then, in every case, the men noticed a dark swelling on their necks, under their arms, or in their groin. At first, the lump was no bigger than a grape. Practically overnight, however, it grew to the size of an egg. Then dark and reddish spots appeared on the dockworkers' bodies. The men became overwhelmed with pain and fever and thirst. In the final stages, they vomited and grew delirious. Many died within 72 hours of first feeling the strange chill.

Then the disease moved swiftly into the town of Messina, killing 10, then 20, then more than

50 people a day. Every time someone died, the church bells tolled. Within three weeks of the arrival of the deadly ships, the church bells rang nonstop. Terrified, the people of Messina fled their homes, often leaving all their belongings behind and their front doors wide open. They rushed to neighboring cities, where they believed they'd escape this evil disease.

But in every instance, the chill followed those who fled. Soon, hundreds—and then thousands—were dying all over Sicily. In some towns, more than half of the people died. And with every day, the disease swept farther north and moved on into other European countries.

What had happened? Where had this terror of death come from? Everyone knew that the Italian sailors had brought the illness with them, but where had they caught it? And how had they given it to the people of Sicily? Slowly, a story drifted over the miles from Asia.

Italian merchants had built a thriving city on the northern shore of the Black Sea, in the area of eastern Europe that is now Ukraine. This port city, called Caffa, served as an important stop on the Silk Road, the overland trading route on which silk and other valuable goods were carried from eastern Asia to Europe. From Caffa, where the Silk Road ended, Italian sailors loaded their ships and headed back to Europe to sell their exotic goods to eager customers.

For more than fifty years, the Mongols, who

ruled Caffa, had allowed the Italians to run Caffa as if they owned it. After all, an increase of trade benefited the Mongols as much as it benefited the Italians. Still, many Mongols were not happy with the situation. They felt that the Italians were intruders. Over the course of several years, brawls between the two groups led to more serious fighting and the death of thousands of people. Sometimes the Italians sought safety in Caffa, with its high stone walls that kept the Mongols out. The Mongols responded, however, by surrounding the city. They believed that sooner or later the Italians would have to come out.

One such siege began in 1346. But this time something was different. Many of the Mongol soldiers were terribly sick with a ghastly and mysterious disease. Many died within three days of noticing a black lump on their body. Soon, there were more bodies than the Mongols could bury, and the rotting corpses seemed to spread the disease faster. In terror and anger, the Mongols came up with a grisly plan.

One by one, corpses were placed on catapults and flung high into the air and over the walls of Caffa. Many of the bodies were so diseased and rotted that they exploded when they hit the streets and buildings of Caffa. The horrified Italians rushed to either bury the broken remains or dump them over the walls into the Black Sea. But it was too late. The dreaded disease took hold almost immediately. No one knows for sure, but some reports claimed that the disease nearly wiped out the entire city—tens of thousands of people died. In desperation, ship owners and sailors sailed away, hoping to escape death. But the disease sailed with them. And then it spread across Europe.

Disease and hardship were not new to most Europeans. They had suffered wars, famine, years of terribly cold and wet weather known as the "Little Ice Age," and an assortment of killer illnesses. But nobody had ever seen anything like this. Many people were certain that it was the end of the world.

"It created such fear," a friar in Italy wrote, "that if a son fell ill, his own father refused to stay with him. If the father did dare come near him, he was sure to die himself after three days. Whole households died, right down to the cats and the cattle."

As the mysterious plague spread, drastic measures were taken. Those who were dying were routinely abandoned with no one to comfort them in their final hours. In some cities, when plague was discovered in a household, the house was boarded up from the outside. The living were left with the dead, to die in the darkness. Sometimes, the townspeople set fire to these houses. But the surest way, people thought, to escape this plague was to run from it.

And anyone who had enough money rushed off to the countryside or to other parts of Europe, farther north, where no illness had yet been reported.

And so, in this way, the disease was carried to nearly every part of Europe. Since records were not kept, it's hard to know exactly how many people died. However, it's estimated that within five years 30 to 60 percent of the *entire population* of the continent of Europe was killed by this gruesome plague. If this happened in the United States today, that would be equal to 100 to 200 million people dying. In every family of four, at least one or two members would be gone. Everyone would lose several friends. You'd be lucky to have even a 50 percent chance of survival.

As hard as this is for us to imagine today, it was even more baffling to people in the mid-1300s.

"I wish I had never been born, or at least had died before these times," wrote the great Italian poet, Petrarch. "When has any such thing been heard or seen? The houses are left vacant, cities are deserted, and fields are too small for all the dead. . . ."

By the time the plague reached Scandinavia in the far north, the disease had become so fierce that it sometimes swept through towns and killed every single person. In one town, the only survivor was a young girl who disappeared into the woods. Years later, she was discovered, a wild and frightened young woman who had somehow survived on her own.

Why, Europeans wondered, was this happening?

Many truly believed that this plague had been sent by God as punishment for their wicked behavior. In response, thousands of men and women walked from town to town, beating themselves and each other with metal-tipped whips. Blood streamed down their backs and legs. Sometimes they whipped one another into unconsciousness. They hoped that God would see them punishing themselves and spare them from the disease.

Many others believed that the sickness came from the devil or some other evil power. It was common to believe in witches and other agents of evil during the 1300s. Countless men and women were killed by townspeople simply for being different. These people were assumed to be working for the devil. Mentally ill, elderly, handicapped, and mentally challenged people were often targets. Many of these unfortunate victims were drowned, stoned, or tortured to death.

However, the most frequent target for blame was Jewish people. Jews had long been mistreated in Europe. They were thought of as outsiders in a society that was almost totally Christian. Some people called Jews "Christ-killers" and accused them of ridiculous and horrible crimes, such as killing babies as sacrifices to the devil. Others believed that Jews were secretly plotting to take over all of Europe.

In any event, everyone wanted someone to blame for this terrible plague. And Jewish people were the easiest target. Because many Jews followed religious laws about their food and drink, they often did not use the same wells for water that the rest of the townspeople used. Suddenly, like wildfire, rumors began spreading that Jews had infected wells throughout Europe. It was all part of their evil plot!

Jewish people were hunted down, beaten, tortured, and killed. They were forced to wear hats with horns to show their connection to the devil. They were driven from their homes and thrown out on the streets on bitter winter nights. Finally, when people realized that just as many Jews as Christians were dying from the plague, the attacks began slowing down. Still, this would remain the worst massacre of Jewish people for 600 years—until the Holocaust during World War II.

Unable to find someone to blame for this plague, Europeans tried to figure out how to keep from catching what had become commonly known as the "Terrible Death." (It was actually not referred to as the "Black Death" until centuries later. No one is sure how the disease got this name, though it is thought to refer to the black spots that cover the body right before a victim dies.)

"Corrupted and poisonous air must be avoided at all times," one doctor wrote. "To breathe foul air is to breathe in death."

In other words, most doctors in the 1300s believed that if the air smelled bad, it contained terrible diseases. The only problem was that practically *all* of the air in towns and cities smelled bad. There was no sewage or garbage collection. Pigs and cows roamed the streets. Dead animals were left to rot wherever they died. And it was no better at home where most people slept in the same room with their goats and chickens. Add to this the fact that people rarely bathed or changed clothes in the 1300s, and you have one stinky environment.

The solution? Many people firmly believed that if they carried sweet-smelling flowers or spices under their noses at all times, they could ward off the plague. At home, they built huge smoky fires in their fireplaces to "smoke out" the bad smells. One king had two fireplaces built in his bedroom. In the worst heat of the summer, he constantly sat between the two raging fires, believing that the heat and smoke would purify the air.

Doctors also recommended avoiding deep sleep. The foul air, doctors pointed out, could sneak up on unaware sleepers. Looking a sick person in the eye was also discouraged. It was believed that poisoned air could shoot right out of the eyes of a plague victim and attack a healthy person. Drinking a lot of wine and eating raw snake meat were also suggested. One doctor even instructed people to stand on their heads for long periods of time.

Obviously, none of these precautions worked. The plague raged on. Since people were unable to avoid catching it, they demanded a cure.

Naturally, it was impossible for fourteenth century doctors to come up with a cure when they had no idea what was causing the Black Death. So they did mainly what they had always done for diseases that caused fevers and swelling. For more than a thousand years, doctors had believed that these kinds of illnesses were caused by having too much blood in the body. Treatment, then, was what was known as "bloodletting." Doctors cut patients' arteries and drained them of blood. During the Black Death, there was no treatment more popular than bloodletting.

Of course, the combination of the plague and serious loss of blood only made matters worse. Not one person was saved by being drained of so much blood.

In desperation, people turned to witchcraft and magic. It was believed that the word "abracadabra" (still used by magicians today) had magical qualities. Many people printed the word on a cloth, which they wore around their neck for protection. And people who were believed to be witches came to be paid good money for cures. That was certainly a far cry from being blamed for the plague. Suddenly, all kinds of strange cures were being created. One drink that was believed to be a cure contained earthworms, dirt, horse urine, and beer!

But in the end, the only thing that worked was time. By late 1351, the Black Death had finally run its course. More than 75 million people had died, and Europe was just a shell of what it had been only five years earlier. Towns were deserted, castles were empty, and ports were full of abandoned ships. Farms and fields were overgrown. Livestock wandered into the hills, ownerless and hungry.

The same plague would return to Europe 300 years later, in the 1600s. While far fewer people would die during this second epidemic, understanding and treatment of the disease had barely changed. Bloodletting was still used by most doctors. Scientists, of course, had no concept of germs. And most people continued to believe that plagues were the result of bad odors or evil.

Truly, on that late October day in 1347, when the people of Messina had ordered the sick sailors back onto their ships, they must have believed that they were safe. So how had the Black Death gotten from the ships to the town?

It would take another 550 years to piece the puzzle together. In 1347, no one would have believed it. But today we know what happened.

Around 1900 a French scientist named Alexandre Yersin discovered that the Black Death and related plagues were the result of bacteria germs carried by rats. Fleas got the disease when they bit the rats. Then fleas jumped onto humans for a bite, and passed the disease along to them. In the 1300s, when people shared their straw and mud houses with their goats, chickens, and sometimes even pigs, fleas were everywhere. And nearly every house had numerous mice and rats running around.

No one ever thought twice about these rodents—or about the dozen black rats that had scurried down the ropes of the Italian ships to the docks of Messina. These unremarkable visitors had carried the fleas that introduced the plague that would change Europe forever.

# Smallpox: Terrible Instrument of Death

In 1145 B.C., Ramses V, a famous Egyptian pharaoh, died suddenly and mysteriously. He was young, and he had ruled for barely four years. Little information was left behind about what happened to him. All we know is that Ramses V died of a "terrible illness" and that his body was left untouched and unburied for two whole years. Typically, the burial of a ruler in ancient Egypt followed strict rules. Pharaohs were preserved as mummies and then buried within 70 days—no exceptions. But this young pharaoh had not been placed in his tomb for more than 700 days. What had happened?

More than 3,000 years later, scientists carefully unwrapped the body of Ramses V, which had been dried and preserved to perfection. Ramses' arms lay across his chest. His closed eyes and drooping mouth still revealed something of his young face in death. And as researchers removed the cloth from the pharaoh's body, something else still remained: All along Ramses' arms, neck, and shoulders were small raised bumps. They looked like a rash or a very bad case of acne—or smallpox.

Now scientists had a clue, perhaps, as to why this young ruler was left unburied for so long. Smallpox was an extremely contagious and deadly disease. Could it be that those who wrapped Ramses' corpse caught smallpox from him? Perhaps the disease had already spread throughout the kingdom. If so, there may not have been anyone strong enough or well enough to prepare the ruler's tomb, and carry him and his belongings into it. Perhaps *everyone* had died. Some researchers think that, years later, Ramses V was buried by those from neighboring settlements who discovered his mummified corpse.

Smallpox has been described as "the most terrible and complete of all the instruments of death." It is an ancient disease. Scientists agree that it probably first appeared about 12,000 years ago somewhere in northeastern Africa. It was one of the most feared diseases on earth, and there was good reason for that fear. Smallpox spread easily and quickly. One sneeze of an infected person could send out millions of tiny virus germs. Anyone standing near that sneeze was likely to come down with smallpox.

The disease itself seemed innocent enough at

the start. It was not much worse than a mild case of the flu. Then there would be a sudden spike in temperature and some sweating, followed by a fairly quick recovery. Victims might feel almost normal for a day or two. But the worst was about to begin.

"Even the most innocent child became wretched to set eyes upon," a writer in the 1800s said. "Covered entirely in a burning, oozing pox. . . . It is indeed a sight too ghastly to describe."

After the fever passed, a bright red rash spread over most of the body. Then, just as quickly, the rash began to turn into white bumps beneath the skin. As one observer explained, "It looked as though many hundreds of grains of rice were trying to push through the flesh." Many victims also endured these bumps (often called "pustules" or "pox") inside their noses and mouths, and even on their eyes. And wherever the pustules appeared, a fiery burning sensation followed.

Within a day or two, these bumps grew, and filled with a clear fluid. Some days later, the pox would begin to break and start to drain. The pus from the pox had a terrible odor that smelled like rotting flesh. The pus drenched clothes and blankets, and spread the smallpox virus to everything it touched.

After visiting a settlement of sick Native Americans, a colonist in the 1600s wrote, "They lie on their hard mats, the pox breaking and draining and all running into one another. Their skin sticks to the mats they lie on; when they turn on them, a whole side of flesh will fall off at once."

Not everyone who got smallpox died. But the illness nearly always left terrible scars where the skin had rotted off. Whether it killed or not, smallpox was clearly an agonizing and terrifying disease.

When smallpox spread to India and China, the people were so frightened that they created a "smallpox goddess." They hoped that if they worshiped her and made sacrifices to her, she would have mercy on them and not give them the disease. The Chinese were convinced that this deadly goddess was particularly fond of giving the disease to attractive children. She seemed to like to destroy their beautiful faces. Her attacks on the children often took place near the Chinese New Year. As a result, on the days leading up to this celebration, children created ugly paper masks for protection. They wore the masks all day and even slept in them, believing that the goddess would be fooled and pass them by.

But sacrifices and paper masks did nothing to slow down the spread of smallpox. Around A.D. 250, thousands of Chinese died from the disease. For the next thousand years, smallpox went where people went—following trade routes and showing up in countries of Asia, Africa, and

Europe. In 1438, an estimated 50,000 people died of smallpox in Paris. By the 1500s, the disease was considered "endemic" in Europe. A disease that is endemic is always present in a particular area; it never dies out. An example of an endemic disease in the United States is the flu. While smallpox killed millions of people in Europe, many others survived the disease. People who had been sick with smallpox could never catch it again. And some people were able to develop a resistance to the disease without even becoming sick. It's possible that smallpox would have disappeared completely if it could have been contained within Europe. But that was not to be. There was a whole New World just across the Atlantic Ocean.

In 1492, when Christopher Columbus landed on the shores of Hispaniola (the island that is today made up of Haiti and the Dominican Republic), there were nearly one million people living there. Sixty years later, the population had dwindled to fewer than 500 natives.

"They died in great heaps, like bedbugs," one Spanish sailor recalled. "In many places, everyone in a house died. Since it was impossible to bury all the dead, they pulled down the houses over them so that their homes became their tombs."

Spanish explorers introduced the natives to new and shocking things—like horses and guns.

But nothing was as terrifying as the invisible smallpox virus that had traveled across the ocean in the bodies of a few sailors. Without any natural resistance to the disease, the natives were practically wiped out.

Next, the Spanish carried the smallpox virus to the mighty Aztec empire in what is now central Mexico. In six months, nearly half of the Aztecs died. As their numbers fell, the Aztecs wondered why the Spanish soldiers rarely got sick. Some believed that the Spanish god was more powerful than the Aztec gods. The Aztecs thought that perhaps they should just give up. In their severely weakened and frightened state, the Aztecs were easy to defeat. By 1521, Spain ruled most of Mexico. Certainly, the Spanish liked to believe that their strong armies had won this victory. In fact, the greatest and most deadly enemy of the Aztecs had been the invisible smallpox virus.

Within about ten years, much of South America was also conquered by the Spanish and smallpox. The Inca Empire in South America was about 16 million people strong. These natives had developed amazing farming techniques. Their architecture and city designs were so advanced that the Spanish conqueror Francisco Pizarro wrote to his king, "Their cities are so beautiful and have such fine buildings that they would be remarkable even in Spain. It is like looking at a dream."

But the Incas' intelligence, hard work, and magnificent history were no match for the Spaniards' guns and disease. In the end, a Spanish army of fewer than 300 men brought down the Incas as smallpox swept through.

"They died by the hundreds," a witness wrote of the proud Incas. "Corpses were scattered over the fields or piled up in the houses and huts. Soon, the fields overgrew and the herds scattered. Those who escaped the foul disease died from starvation."

In 1600, the lands that would become the United States and Canada were home to 20 million Native Americans. Like the natives of Mexico and South America, these were civilized, intelligent, and usually peaceful people. However, the colonists who settled in and around Boston didn't see the natives that way.

Many colonists thought the Native Americans were evil simply because they looked different and had different habits. And when the natives rightfully grew angry at the colonists for taking over their lands, they were seen as being downright dangerous and worthy of punishment.

"The Indians began to be quarrelsome concerning the boundaries of land," wrote a Boston minister in 1633. "But God ended the quarrel by sending the smallpox to them. Whole towns of them were swept away. In some towns, not one soul remained."

Smallpox did not affect the colonists as tragically as it affected the Native Americans, but epidemics still flared up now and then. One of the worst hit Boston in 1721. By coincidence, it was just about this same time that Europeans had discovered a way to protect themselves from catching smallpox. Actually, the discovery had originally been made by Chinese doctors hundreds of years earlier.

The Chinese knew that someone who survived a bout of smallpox could never catch the disease again. Even if the case had been very mild, the person would be immune to smallpox forever. Why not, doctors wondered, intentionally infect someone with a very, very small amount of the virus? This would create slight symptoms of the disease without killing the patient. Then the patient would be immune.

Chinese doctors tested this idea by scraping scabs off smallpox victims and grinding the scabs into a fine powder. Then, the smallest bit of powder was blown up into the nostrils of a healthy person. As expected, the person became slightly ill for a week or so, and then recovered. Next, the doctors exposed the person to a full dose of smallpox virus. (Most of these "test patients" were prisoners who had no say in the matter.) Much to the excitement of the doctors, none of the test patients got sick again. The doctors had discovered a way to keep people from getting the dreaded disease!

The Chinese and people in some parts of eastern Europe had practiced this method of prevention, known as "inoculation," for centuries. But most western Europeans and Americans had never heard of it. Lady Mary Wortley Montagu, a brilliant and outspoken British woman and wife of a British ambassador, learned about this live-saving procedure—and had her son inoculated—when her family was living in the area that is now Turkey. Then, when the family returned to England, she spoke enthusiastically in favor of the procedure, and she insisted that her three-year-old daughter be inoculated.

Many British people were horrified by the idea of inoculation. It made no sense to infect healthy people, particularly children, with smallpox! Others believed that interfering with the disease was interfering with the will of God. But when the Prince and Princess of Wales put their support behind inoculation, the idea began to catch on in Britain. Instead of blowing scab dust up a person's nose, however, a new method was developed: putting a small bit of virus into a cut on the arm. This worked just as well, and it didn't seem quite as disgusting to the British.

People in the American colonies were also afraid to try inoculation at first. But after a famous doctor inoculated 280 patients and only 6 died, people began lining up for the treatment if they could afford it. Benjamin Franklin encouraged inoculations, and eventually free inoculations were provided for the poor. In time, George Washington would insist on having Revolutionary War soldiers inoculated. Washington was all too familiar with the pain of smallpox. In paintings, we can see the scars and pock marks that the disease had left on his cheeks.

Before long, more and more colonists were becoming safe from the smallpox virus—but not the Native Americans. No one was very concerned about protecting these "savages," as they were called. In fact, as settlers began moving farther west, there were even plots to spread smallpox among tribes in an attempt to get them out of the way.

"Could it not be planned to send the smallpox among these tribes of Indians?" a British commander wrote to one of his colonels.

"I will try to infect the Indians with some blankets that may fall into their hands," the colonel wrote back.

Several weeks later, two dirty blankets and some soiled handkerchiefs from a smallpox hospital were handed over as "gifts" to two unsuspecting Native American chiefs. No one can say for certain whether these gifts led to the terrible smallpox outbreaks that soon followed. But by the end of the 1700s, many tribes had been entirely wiped out. The 20 million Native Americans that had lived proudly and in good health for thousands of years in North America had been reduced to barely one million.

Inoculation, without a doubt, had saved many lives. Still, it had its drawbacks. Everyone who received the treatment became at least slightly sick with smallpox. Sometimes, people even died after being inoculated. If only there was a way to protect people without making them sick first.

In 1796, that way was discovered. A British doctor named Edward Jenner performed an experiment. He had long heard that people who milked cows caught a mild skin disease called "cowpox," but never became sick with smallpox. Cowpox created pustules on the hands after milking cows that were infected with the disease. Victims might run a slight fever, but that was the extent of their symptoms. And the pustules generally disappeared in a week, leaving no scars.

Jenner deliberately infected an eight-year-old boy with cowpox. About six weeks later, Jenner injected the same boy with smallpox. The boy remained perfectly healthy! Jenner named this treatment *vaccine*, from the Latin word meaning "of cows." Within the next several years, Italians discovered how to grow the cowpox virus in cows. When pustules formed on the cows' skin, the pus was collected and used for vaccines.

Millions of doses of vaccine were produced in this way. By 1900, smallpox was disappearing from parts of the world.

Scattered outbreaks of smallpox continued well into the 1900s. In fact, 300 million people worldwide died from smallpox in the 1900s alone. However, in 1967, the World Health Organization decided to focus on completely destroying smallpox once and for all. Doctors and health workers traveled to the poorest and most remote parts of the planet. Wherever smallpox reared its horrible head, workers rushed to vaccinate the people. It took over a decade, but in 1979 the long-awaited announcement was made: After thousands of years and millions of deaths, smallpox was finally gone from the earth.

Well, almost gone.

In laboratories in Moscow, Russia, and Atlanta, Georgia, there are two small vials of the smallpox virus. The virus is kept so that it can be studied. But many people believe that the smallpox virus in these vials should also be destroyed. After all, there is still no cure—just a 200-year-old vaccine made from cow pus. What if these vials should fall into the wrong hands? Could smallpox again be used to kill people in the same way it had reportedly been used to kill Native Americans?

Fear of this possibility is not taken lightly.

"The labs are protected with alarm systems and closed-circuit televisions," a director from the World Health Organization said. "The vials are locked within two safes and are frozen solid in liquid nitrogen."

And what is the final safeguard against the chance of smallpox entering the earth again?

Three sets of keys are needed to get to the vials. Three different people hold these keys, and all three key holders' identities are known to only one other person.

"We take it pretty seriously," the director explained.

## CHAPTER 3

# Deadly Summer in Philadelphia

"I'm telling you that things here in Philadelphia need to change!" thundered Reverend Helmuth. "There is far too much drinking, gambling, and laziness."

His friend Dr. Benjamin Rush sat across from him sipping tea. Rush sighed. He didn't really think the people of Philadelphia were all that bad. "It's this heat and the drought," Rush said with a shrug. "No one feels like working. Life will return to normal once the weather changes."

But Helmuth shook his head and wagged his finger in Rush's face. "Don't you see? This is only the beginning. We will all feel the burning of God's anger before it is all over."

It was August 3, 1793, and it was yet another unusually hot day in Philadelphia, Pennsylvania. It hadn't rained for weeks, and the air hung heavy and full of bad odors. The stench was particularly bad this summer. Although there was no sewer system, summer rains usually swept garbage and sewage into the Delaware River. This year, however, the streets were reeking with old food, human waste, and even dead animals.

Making matters worse, the heat brought far more insects than usual. Roaches and flies scuttled and buzzed in every house. Thick clouds of mosquitoes buzzed and bit constantly. A worker near the Arch Street dock noticed that when oil was accidentally spilled into water containing mosquito eggs, the mosquitoes never hatched. He placed a notice in the paper about his discovery. However, most people preferred to put up with the bugs rather than waste oil. It was just a few more mosquito bites. The summer would be over soon enough.

Dr. Rush didn't really agree with his minister friend and his predictions of doom. Still, something didn't feel right. Rare and unusual illnesses kept popping up. The flu, which was common as a winter ailment, had sickened hundreds in July. And then, just three days ago, a poor French sailor had suffered from some kind of terrible illness that had caused seizures and death within 72 hours. He had been staying at an inn near Water Street by the wharf.

Despite the problems, in many ways 1793 had been a good year for Philadelphia. Trade was increasing. Many products, such as sugar cane and coffee, were imported from Caribbean islands. People came, too, along with the products, seeking refuge from political unrest. At first, there was just a trickle of refugees, but then they arrived by the thousands, on ship after ship.

After parting ways with his friend, the doctor walked slowly along Water Street. He was deep in thought about heat, illness, and doom when a particularly hideous smell filled the air.

Rush clapped a hand over his nose. “What is that horrible stink?” he asked a stranger passing by.

“Rotten coffee,” the stranger said, waving toward the wharf. “A bad shipment came in, and they’ve dumped it on the docks. I wouldn’t get too close to it. They say several men living near Water Street have died from it already.”

Rush was confused by what the stranger meant. Had they died from the same illness as the unfortunate French sailor? The next day, he found out.

When Dr. Rush answered a panicked knocking at his door, a nervous messenger said, “Dr. Rush, you’ve been asked to come quickly. Another person is dying on Water Street!”

This time, it was a young woman named Catherine. Two other doctors had been called to tend to her, but when her symptoms continued to worsen, they sent for Dr. Rush. The young woman looked terrible. Her eyes and skin were an alarming yellow, and blood trickled from her nose. A fever was burning her up, and she tossed from side to side. Every ten minutes or so, she grabbed her stomach and cried out that her stomach felt like it was on fire. Then she vomited a thick black substance.

The two other doctors backed away in horror. They had never seen anything like this.

"It's that rotted coffee on the wharf," they agreed. "The smell of it is sickening everyone who lives near it!"

But Dr. Rush moved closer to Catherine and examined her. Unlike the other doctors, he *had* seen this disease before—nearly thirty years earlier in Philadelphia. It was yellow fever. When Rush suggested this to the other doctors, they strongly disagreed. Yellow fever was a savage disease that could spread incredibly rapidly, but it occurred mainly in tropical areas. Worst of all, there was no treatment and no cure for it. Most likely, the doctors were terrified to even consider that Rush might be right.

"It's nothing more than that vile smell," one doctor said, waving Rush off. For more than a thousand years, it had been believed that bad odors could cause fevers and even death. Surely that's all this was. Once the coffee was cleaned up, the disease would end.

But days after the wharf had been completely cleaned, people were still dying. By mid-August, a dozen people died each day. The symptoms were always the same, and the deaths were terribly gruesome. And by the end of August, the illness had spread well beyond Water Street. The daily death count numbered twenty or more. The rumbling of the death carts—wooden carts used to take corpses away—filled the streets.

"Fly from it!" Dr. Rush advised the residents of Philadelphia. "Leave before this fever kills you!"

Everyone was still reluctant to believe that this was the feared yellow fever, but there was no denying that death was spreading rapidly throughout the city. This was an exceptionally disgusting sickness. The stories of convulsions, bright yellow eyes, and black and bloody vomit were too much. Suddenly, everyone was in a panic of packing, closing up homes and businesses, slamming doors, and rushing to the countryside. During the course of the fever, more than 20,000 people would leave Philadelphia. This was nearly half of its population in 1793.

Those who were left behind were mostly poor people who had no place to go. People with more money could afford to rent villas, rooms, or country homes until the fever disappeared. Still, the mayor of Philadelphia bravely stayed in his city. And many doctors, including Benjamin Rush, stayed behind to help battle this terrible disease. It was hard to figure out what to do, though. Most of the doctors still refused to believe that the disease around them was yellow fever.

"Quarantine!" many doctors ordered. "Anyone with the disease must be locked away from others until we figure out what this is."

"Lock *yourselves* away!" others argued. "Shut off the outside world. Do not even venture into the streets or open a window."

Some doctors recommended wearing vinegar-soaked clothing, chewing garlic all day, and smoking tobacco heavily. They felt this would keep the foul air that contained the fever from getting too close to the body. Still other doctors called for cleaning Philadelphia's air by blasting cannons, guns, and fireworks. Smoke, they believed, would clear out anything dangerous in the air.

Most people were terribly confused about what to do. Everyone was terrified. The few people who ventured outside walked in the middle of the empty streets instead of on the sidewalks. They were afraid that if they even walked too close to buildings that contained sick people, they'd get sick, too.

One family shut itself inside its small house and nailed boards across the windows. Several times a day, the father shot six rounds from his musket into the living area to clear the air. The mother constantly wiped down everything, including the children, with a vinegar and rotten egg mixture. Because they refused to leave their home, the family soon ran out of food. In desperation, they ate six pet birds and the family dog.

In spite of all these precautions, people continued dying at an alarming rate. By mid-September, forty to fifty people were dying every day. Soon there were no workers left to bury all of the bodies being taken to the graveyards. Corpses piled up and rotted, fouling the air even more. Because people were afraid to care for one another, some victims died alone in their homes and weren't found for weeks. Worst of all, though, were the hundreds of sick beggars who had no homes. These unfortunate people crawled through the streets moaning, covered with blood and vomit.

Conditions in Philadelphia were so horrible and frightening that farmers refused to enter the city with their daily deliveries of food. This created a new problem: Those left in Philadelphia were faced not only with a raging deadly epidemic, but also with the real possibility of starvation. The mayor ordered all sick beggars to be taken to a nearby vacant mansion called Bush Hill. The mansion's owner was in England, and though the mayor had no right to take over the mansion, he felt he had no choice. The local hospitals would not treat beggars, and these poor people could not be left to die in the streets.

Bush Hill turned out to be yet another nightmare, however. Only three doctors could be persuaded to tend to the sick beggars. Within a week, two of the doctors died and the third fell ill. Soon the mansion was little more than a dumping ground for dying men, women, and children.

"The sick, dying, and dead were all thrown together," one visitor observed. "It was . . . hell on earth, a terribly gruesome scene. It was, in fact, a great human slaughterhouse."

As the epidemic was nearing its peak, a strange event took place. Out of a clear morning sky, a meteor fell to earth. It landed with a thunderous boom right in the middle of Third Street in Philadelphia. No one had ever seen anything like it. Many people believed this was a bad omen, indicating that things were only going to get worse.

Others believed that this was a sign from God. Only recently, the United States had become a new country after the colonists had fought the American Revolution and won their freedom from the British. For most Americans, it was a time of great pride, but there were still many people who felt the war had been wrong. Those people felt that yellow fever was God's punishment. But why would God target his punishment on Philadelphia? Many believed that it was because, in 1793, Philadelphia was the young nation's capital. The headquarters of the young country's government had not yet moved to Washington, D.C.

Even President George Washington became increasingly nervous. He had been determined not to shut down the federal government.

However, when the Secretary of the Treasury, six clerks, and numerous other officials became ill, Washington began packing. Within 24 hours, he and his wife, Martha, were headed back to their farm in Virginia.

"Every day, Philadelphia becomes more and more fatal," he wrote.

"The black man simply does not get sick!" Dr. Rush announced excitedly. "God has seen fit to give him a special resistance."

Benjamin Rush spoke to a large group called the Free African Society. This was an organization created by black people to help black people. Slavery was still thriving in many states, but in Philadelphia, there were more than 3,000 free blacks. Rush was pleading with these free blacks to help their white neighbors, who were dying at a rate of up to 100 per day.

Nearly every black person present could probably have found a good reason to turn his or her back. Blacks in Philadelphia may have had their freedom, but they were still very poorly treated. They were denied basic rights, given the worst-paying jobs, and even refused entry into many churches and schools. Still, in this time of crisis in their city, the members of the Free African Society helped without even thinking twice.

"It was our duty to do all the good we could to our fellow mortals," the leaders of the Society explained.

From that moment on, black volunteers ventured into the streets, down dark alleys, and into the parts of Philadelphia where there was the most sickness. While nearly all other community leaders, church groups, elected officials, and aid organizations had left the city in terror, black people stayed and helped. They worked long hours for little or no money. They bravely endured their patients' horrific final days, bringing them water and comfort to the very end.

"I don't know what the people would do," wrote one doctor who had stayed in the city, "if it was not for the Negroes. They are the only nurses."

But although Benjamin Rush had been right about believing that blacks would help, he had been dead wrong about something else: Blacks were *not* immune to yellow fever. Day by day, many fearless and generous members of the Free African Society began dying. And things began looking more hopeless than ever. It was at this point that Dr. Rush went into a mad frenzy of searching for a cure.

Rush tried extreme bloodletting first. Bloodletting, the practice of draining blood out of the body in order to allow bodily fluids to "flow more freely," had been practiced by doctors for more than 2,000 years. The fact that it never really cured anything didn't seem to stop doctors from using it. Rush bled patients until they fainted. Naturally, this only killed them more quickly.

Then Rush tried boiling vinegar baths, wine mixed with chemicals, and ointments that burned the skin until it blistered. Nothing worked. Finally, however, Rush was sure he had uncovered the magical combination. It was understood that yellow fever caused internal bleeding and filled the intestines and stomach with "bad" blood. Rush figured that if a patient were given a poison strong enough to produce extreme vomiting and diarrhea, most of the bad blood would be flushed out of the body. This would be followed by heavy bloodletting. In the end, no bad blood would be left.

Amazingly, Rush's plan seemed to cure his first two patients. Then, according to Rush, 29 of 30 people treated with this process went from their deathbed to complete health. It is hard to know whether the fever itself was simply no longer as deadly or whether Rush was exaggerating. Certainly, the "cure" would have been as deadly as the disease. Other doctors in Philadelphia knew that Rush's methods were not curing people. He became something of a joke among his fellow physicians.

But when Rush became ill with yellow fever and cured *himself*, lines of sick people formed outside his door. More than 150 patients a day were poisoned and bled by Rush and his assistants. Blood flowed through the dry, empty streets in front of Rush's home. Dr. Rush was so confident of his cure that he proclaimed, "I have proved that yellow fever, when treated in this new way, is no worse than the common cold!"

But again, Benjamin Rush was wrong. Yellow fever would continue to plague Philadelphia until, it was noted with curiosity, the first hard frost fell on the city late that year. Then, for some reason, yellow fever disappeared. Slowly and cautiously, people trickled back from the countryside. Doors were unlocked, musty homes were aired out, and businesses were reopened. Life returned to the great city.

Still, many people remained haunted by the horror of that summer of 1793.

"Sometimes I lose myself in looking back upon the ocean which I have passed," Dr. Rush would later write. "I weep reflecting upon the friends I have lost and the distress I have witnessed and how I was unable to help."

However, Dr. Benjamin Rush helped in ways he would never know. He had kept very detailed notes about his patients. He described everything from their symptoms to their expressions in death. And more than a few times, he curiously noticed "tiny reddish bumps that resemble mosquito bites." Perhaps he thought nothing of this detail. But more than a century later it became an important clue that helped unravel the mystery of yellow fever.

As it turns out, the residents of Philadelphia would have done well to have "wasted" a little oil to prevent mosquito eggs from hatching during that hot summer when bugs were so numerous. No one would have believed it in 1793, but the virus that causes yellow fever is transmitted by the tiny mosquito. When a female mosquito bites a person who is infected with yellow fever, it takes in the virus when it sucks the victim's blood. Then, when the mosquito bites a healthy person, it passes the virus into that person's bloodstream. In fact, yellow fever cannot be spread from person to person—only from mosquito to person!

Yellow fever occurs primarily in tropical climates—parts of South America, Africa, and tropical islands. Yellow fever had been carried to Philadelphia by the refugees who had come from the Caribbean. When mosquitoes bit them— and then bit Philadelphians—they spread the dreaded disease. New cases of yellow fever disappeared with the first frost, because the mosquitoes could not survive the cold temperatures.

Today, a vaccine exists that can prevent transmission of the yellow fever virus. Does this make us completely safe? Not at all.

For one thing, since yellow fever has not been a real threat in the United States for more than 100 years, the country produces very little vaccine and has very little available. It would take months to produce thousands of doses of vaccine if it were suddenly needed in the United States.

But more importantly, we still have one thing in common with those who lived in fear of yellow fever in Philadelphia in 1793: There remains no cure for this horrible disease. And mosquitoes can still spread it very quickly.

"If it begins again in this country," stated a health official, "it's probably going to spread very rapidly. It's a modern-day time bomb. We're just sitting here waiting for it to happen."

## CHAPTER 4

# Fear and Paralysis: The Story of Polio

In 1950, a young girl was wading with friends in a river near their small town of Wytheville, Virginia. It was a very hot summer day, so when the girl suddenly broke out in a sweat, she didn't think much of it. But when she suddenly got a terrible headache, she decided to go sit on the riverbank in the shade.

"As I walked out of the water, it felt like something was tugging at my leg," the girl recalled. "When I looked down, I noticed that I was dragging my leg. All at once, I couldn't feel it at all."

In less than 48 hours, both of the girl's legs were paralyzed. And she wasn't the only person who was having this experience. The town's two ambulances were constantly busy, taking child after child to the hospital in nearby Roanoke. The quiet town of Wytheville had been struck with a polio epidemic. Alarming reports filled the newspapers. People who had to drive through Wytheville rolled up their windows and drove as fast as they could. Some people even put their hands over their mouths and noses as they sped through.

Terrified parents of sick children were told to destroy anything their sick child had touched. All over town, piles of clothing, toys, books, and bedding were hauled out to backyards and set on fire.

"No one knew what to do," a woman later remembered. "That was what was so frightening about polio. No one ever knew how bad it would get. It might just cause a little fever, or it might paralyze you . . . or worse."

Polio was hardly a new disease. It had been around for thousands of years. Scientists have uncovered 6,000-year-old skeletons with twisted and bent leg bones, one sign of polio. But there had never been an outbreak in the United States until the 1900s. Doctors were baffled. It seemed that polio had appeared just when major efforts were being made to keep cities clean, provide sanitation, and stress the importance of hand washing.

Why would cleaner conditions create polio epidemics? Years later, scientists figured it out.

It turns out that before indoor plumbing made cleaner surroundings possible, infants were exposed to the polio virus all the time. However, polio is not particularly dangerous to infants.

The exposure might cause a mild fever, and then the illness would disappear in a few days. But even that slight illness caused infants to build up a resistance to polio. The infants produced antibodies, making them immune to polio for life.

But by 1900, cities and towns in the United States were much cleaner. Sewage no longer ran in the streets, and outhouses had been replaced with indoor plumbing. Doctors realized that staying clean and washing regularly protected people from disease. But it also kept most infants from coming in contact with the polio virus and having a chance to build up resistance to it. Then, when the child was several years older and, by chance, *did* come in contact with the virus, the disease could be devastating.

Polio seemed to target children between the ages of 5 and 12, but not all of its victims were young. Its most famous victim was 39 years old. He was an attractive young man from a very wealthy family. And in the summer of 1921, many Americans believed that this young man might be president some day. His name was Franklin Delano Roosevelt, and during that summer his life would change forever.

Following a busy vacation day filled with swimming, boating, and even a two-mile run, Roosevelt sat down to read a newspaper. Suddenly, he felt a strange numbness and ache throughout his body.

"I'd never quite felt that way," Roosevelt later said. "I tried to persuade myself that it was just tired muscles."

But it wasn't. Two days later, both of Roosevelt's legs were paralyzed. Within a week, the young man who had loved running and dancing and football found himself in a wheelchair. Roosevelt refused to feel sorry for himself. Immediately, he began looking for anything that might help heal his lifeless legs. He'd read about a boy whose legs had gotten better through hydrotherapy—the use of warm water. In response, Roosevelt took a trip to a Georgia inn known for its natural hot springs. Roosevelt was so impressed with the springs and the comfort of the warm water that he bought the inn in 1926 for nearly $200,000.

The inn would become the Georgia Warm Springs Foundation, and Roosevelt opened it up to anyone with polio, regardless of their ability to pay for a room or services. Roosevelt splashed and played with the many children who visited. As the father of six, Roosevelt ached for these stricken young people. He was determined that his foundation would work to help find a cure for polio.

However, when Roosevelt became governor of New York in 1928 and then began his campaign for President of the United States, he did not have the time to devote to Warm Springs. Roosevelt turned to his law partner,

Basil O'Connor, and asked him to take over the foundation.

"I thought he was crazy," O'Connor later admitted. "At first, I couldn't have been less interested. I was never a public do-gooder. But then I started enjoying it."

O'Connor may not have been a "do-gooder," but he was very good at raising money. He knew a lot of very rich people, and he persuaded them to donate money to help with polio research. Scientists were already experimenting with ideas for a vaccine, but their work was very expensive. The only people who could afford to give big contributions were the rich—then came the Wall Street Crash of 1929.

With the arrival of the Great Depression, many wealthy people were no longer able to donate large sums of money. Research nearly came to a standstill as scientists waited for financial help. But, of course, polio did not take a break from attacking its victims. In fact, outbreaks were becoming more and more frequent. By the mid-1930s, thousands of children had been crippled by polio, and thousands more were very sick.

Franklin Roosevelt was now President of the United States. As much as possible, he tried to avoid being photographed in his wheelchair or on crutches. He never talked much about polio, because he believed that Americans didn't want to be reminded that their leader had been crippled by it. He thought he should appear strong. When he had to appear in front of a large crowd or when he was being filmed, he put heavy metal braces on his legs. Then he leaned slightly against one of his aides and walked slowly. Many Americans didn't even realize how badly polio had damaged the president's legs.

In 1938, however, Roosevelt's distancing himself from polio came to an end. A Hollywood star and close friend of Roosevelt's, Eddie Cantor, came up with an idea for a polio fundraising campaign. "We could call it the March of Dimes," Cantor suggested. In the 1930s, the name of a popular news program shown in movie theaters (even before television!) was *The March of Time.* Cantor knew that people would be intrigued by the sound-alike name.

"We could ask people to send dimes directly to the president at the White House!" Cantor said excitedly in a meeting with Basil O'Connor. "After all, who can't afford a dime?"

At first, O'Connor thought Cantor's idea was dreadful. Send envelopes full of dimes to the White House? Had Eddie Cantor lost his mind? But when O'Connor laughingly asked Roosevelt about it, the president surprised everyone by saying, "Go ahead."

Movie stars eagerly jumped on board to support and promote this new March of Dimes campaign. Even the actor who played the Lone Ranger in a 1938 movie filmed a heartfelt appeal to all Americans to pitch in and send dimes to the White House. No one was sure how popular this unusual campaign would be. The supervisor at the White House mailroom mentioned to his workers that there might be an increase in mail following the promotion of this campaign.

"Basically," this supervisor said later, "the roof fell in on me. We usually handled 5,000 letters a day. Three days into the March of Dimes, we received 150,000 letters."

Letters filled the hallways, and dimes sat in huge piles on every available desk. Roosevelt was filmed opening letter after letter and pouring out rivers of coins. In the end, 2,680,000 dimes were sent to the White House. In addition, thousands of envelopes included checks and small bills. Millions of Americans had sent not only money, they had also sent a resounding message: We want an end to polio!

Although the idea of sending dimes to the White House would not be repeated, the dime would become a symbol of the fight against polio. After all, *everyone* could afford a dime. Everyone could help.

But with the 1940s came World War II. Some feared that the fight against polio would be forgotten. It wasn't. In movie theaters across the nation, March of Dimes buckets were passed like church collection plates, and thousands of dollars were received.

At first, not a lot of the money raised went into vaccine research. More funds went into treatments like warm water therapy, massage, and leg bracing. Many Americans were not convinced that vaccines were safe. The theory behind a vaccine, of course, is that injecting a very small bit of the virus into a healthy person will cause the person to build up immunity to the disease. This had worked for other diseases, but polio was trickier. Even the smallest bit of polio was dangerous.

In 1935, a trial vaccination was given to thousands of children. It had worked on monkeys, and scientists felt confident that it would also protect children. Perhaps it did keep some children safe from the polio virus, but fifteen children actually caught polio in towns where no polio cases had been reported. They had become sick from the vaccine! When ten vaccinated children died, the vaccine was destroyed. Perhaps, people thought, it would be better to spend money on treating those who were already sick.

One of the most expensive treatments used to help keep children alive was a machine called the "iron lung." Since polio attacked the muscles, some children lost the use of the muscles that controlled their breathing. Their lungs were healthy, but they were unable to take a breath. In many cases, as children grew healthier, their ability to breathe returned. But until then, they were placed inside an iron lung.

To many, nothing was more frightening than the image of the iron lung. Picture a big metal barrel with a few windows, knobs, and scary pressure gauges on either side. Now imagine being slid into this horizontal barrel until only your head remains outside the barrel, at one end. Plates are clamped close to your neck, and your head and throat are cushioned and closed off from the rest of your body. A loud swooshing sound begins as the air pressure inside the barrel forces your chest to rise and fall, sending air into your lungs.

Imagine spending the next year—or longer—inside this barrel. Life inside an iron lung was the fate of thousands of polio victims. At the height of the polio outbreaks of the 1940s and 1950s, huge wards would be filled with row upon row of iron lungs, just a few feet apart. Some patients would never return to life outside an iron lung. As of 2008, thirty Americans who had been struck with polio as children in the 1940s or 1950s were still living in an iron lung.

In 1945, polio lost its greatest activist. Franklin Roosevelt died suddenly of a stroke while vacationing, by chance, at Warm Springs in Georgia. After Roosevelt's death, Basil O'Connor was more determined than ever to find and fund scientists who could develop a safe polio vaccine. Scientists had continued to work, but understanding how to make a safe vaccine remained a mystery. Only months before

Roosevelt had died, he had told O'Connor how badly he longed for this discovery.

"It tears me apart to see the children and their suffering," he had said. "There are far too many being brought down by this horrible disease."

"Far too many" was the truth. By the late 1940s, polio was attacking an average of 35,000 Americans a year. Whirlpool baths and iron lungs could offer relief and aid, but it was time to put an end to this growing number of victims. It was time for somebody to unravel the mystery and create a safe vaccine. That somebody would be Dr. Jonas Salk.

Jonas Salk was the son of Russian immigrants. Like many other people in the early 1900s, his parents had come to the United States in search of a better life. Mostly, they hoped the United States would offer their children more opportunity than they would have had in Russia. Jonas grew up in New York City, in an apartment that his mother kept spotlessly clean.

Young Jonas was very thin and small for his age. Making matters worse, his eyesight was so bad that he had to wear thick glasses beginning in the third grade. He might have been the kind of boy that bigger kids bullied, but when Jonas was 12, he was chosen to attend a special school for highly intelligent teens. There he was surrounded by other young people who studied and worked as hard as he did.

Salk loved two things: solving mysteries and helping people. In the neighborhood where he grew up, Salk often saw polio-stricken young people walking with crutches. He was both upset and intrigued. Why hadn't anyone discovered a way to stop polio? By the time he reached college, Salk had made up his mind: He would become a medical scientist and try to unravel the mysteries of diseases.

By the mid-1940s, Salk had developed an outstanding reputation through his work on flu vaccines. This caught the attention of leaders of the National Foundation for Infantile Paralysis. In 1947, the NFIP gave Salk and the University of Pittsburgh, where he worked, a grant for $148,000 to develop a polio vaccine. Although this was barely enough to get started, other grants followed. In the end, it would take $1,250,000—in addition to 30,000 monkeys for testing!

Salk was certainly not the only scientist searching for a vaccine. By 1950, the year polio swept through Wytheville, the quest for a vaccine discovery had become something of a race. Salk's greatest competitor was an older scientist named Albert Sabin. Sabin had made some important discoveries about how polio was spread from person to person, and he felt his ideas for a vaccine were better than Salk's.

Jonas Salk thought that the vaccine should contain killed virus, not live virus. He thought live virus was too dangerous. After all, it had been vaccines with live virus that had made children sick in 1935. Sabin, on the other hand, believed that Salk was wasting time and money. How could dead virus create antibodies in humans? Sabin scoffed at Salk's unusual approach. In fact, a lot of scientists did. It seemed like a crazy idea.

But Salk paid no attention. He believed that even though the virus was dead, it would fool the body into producing antibodies. He had seen this happen with other diseases. In addition, Salk had a sense—a feeling about the virus—that was hard to explain. "I picture myself as the virus and try to sense what it would be like," he once said with a shrug and a smile in an interview.

Finally, in 1953, Salk thought his vaccine was ready. He was so certain that the vaccine was safe that he tested the first batch on himself and his family. Success! Salk, his wife, and his three sons remained well and began producing the antibodies that would forever keep them immune to polio.

News of this vaccine swept across the nation. Salk appeared on the cover of *Time* magazine. It was all very exciting, but the vaccine still needed to be field tested. This means that it needed to be tested on a wide variety of volunteers—both young and old from a broad geographic area. Today, it may be hard to imagine eagerly volunteering to get a shot of a vaccine that is still being tested. But in 1953, people were so tired and afraid of polio that they rushed to get in line. Most parents did not think twice about allowing their young children to be "polio pioneers," as they were proudly called. In addition, more than 100 million people in the United States—more than half of the country's population—had contributed to the March of Dimes. They were ready to try this vaccine that in a very real sense they had helped to develop.

By early 1954, nearly 2 million Americans had received the Salk vaccine. Most were children. It would take a year of waiting, and looking at results, before the vaccine could be called a success. Although Salk had great confidence in his vaccine, the success of the test depended so much more than the vaccine itself. Several drug companies had to manufacture the vaccine correctly, and thousands of doctors and nurses injected it. He wanted no disaster like the one that had occurred with the 1935 trial.

"He was not just a scientist worried about an experiment," a nurse who worked with Salk explained. "He was a man deeply concerned about the human importance of the experiment."

Finally, in the spring of 1955, a great gathering of scientists, doctors, and reporters took place at the University of Michigan. It was time for the official announcement about the vaccine.

"I felt like I was in the eye of a hurricane," Salk said. "All this swirling was going on. It was the moment that everything changed."

It was, indeed. Salk's vaccine worked! After thousands of years and millions of victims, a way to stop polio had been discovered. Newspaper reporters literally fell over one another in a rush to get the story out to the world.

Polio rates dropped from 38,000 new cases in the United States in 1954 to about 100 new cases only ten years later. A longtime dream had finally come true.

Salk was not comfortable bragging or drawing attention to himself in the many interviews that followed. Often, he would explain that his discovery was simply the natural result of wanting to solve a mystery.

"You never have an idea of what you might accomplish," he once said. "All that you do is you pursue a question. And see where it leads."

# CHAPTER 5

## A Modern Epidemic: AIDS

"We know you're a queer! Get the hell out of this town!"

Angry shouts shot out of a car as it roared past fourteen-year-old Ryan White in downtown Kokomo, Indiana. Ryan's mother, accompanying Ryan to yet another doctor's appointment, just shook her head.

"Ignore them," she said quietly. "Don't let them upset you."

Ryan didn't look at his mother. He just stared at the ground and mumbled, "I'm not upset."

But he was. That morning at school, he had gone to his locker and found it smashed open. All his books and belongings had been thrown on the floor. Someone had written "fag" in red ink on several folders. Most of the other kids at his high school just walked by and snickered. One older boy threw a pen at Ryan and said, "No one wants you here."

Later, at lunch, Ryan was forced by school officials to sit alone at a table that was some distance from the others. He had to use plastic utensils so that they could be thrown away after he ate. No one wanted to run the risk of using utensils Ryan had used. After lunch, he was told to wait inside in an empty classroom while his classmates played basketball without him. He was even forced to use a separate bathroom and drinking fountain.

Only one year earlier, Ryan had been a happy and popular boy. He ate too much pizza, loved cars, collected comic books, and did the same things any teenager might do. His friends particularly liked his jokes and his positive attitude. People around his Kokomo neighborhood recognized him as their paperboy. But now, many of those same people would not touch the newspapers he delivered. One man even burned them.

What had happened? Had Ryan committed some awful crime? Had he somehow insulted everyone he'd ever known?

Much to the contrary, Ryan was very weak and ill—deathly ill. He had been told that he might not live long. It's hard to imagine that anyone, much less an entire town, would be intentionally cruel to a young person who is terribly sick. But this was 1984, and nobody knew very much about the disease that Ryan carried in his body. All most people knew was that it could kill, and it could not be cured. It's been said that fear breeds hate, and when people looked at Ryan White, they were not just afraid—they were terrified.

In the 1970s, many doctors and scientists were feeling quite confident about their ability to cure most diseases. Some even boldly suggested that the days of epidemics were over. After all, cures or vaccines had been discovered for nearly all of the world's worst contagious diseases. Perhaps there were would be no new plagues.

Then, in 1977, something strange happened. A Danish surgeon, Dr. Grethe Rask, died of an extremely rare form of pneumonia called "pneumocystis." For several years, while working in hospitals in Africa, she had experienced weight loss, fatigue, and other relatively minor symptoms. Eventually, however, she became too weak to continue her work. Doctors could see that her immune system was shutting down, but they couldn't figure out why. Cells known as "T cells" usually swarm the blood and kill invading illnesses. However, Dr. Rask's blood had barely any T cells. That was highly unusual.

After Grethe Rask died, doctors might have just filed her case away as one of those unfortunate medical mysteries that pop up every now and then. However, a few years later, several men in New York City were suffering the same symptoms Rask had suffered: exhaustion and disappearing T cells. Then the men became very sick with a variety of odd diseases that a healthy body could usually fight off.

The oddest disease was a skin cancer called "Kaposi's sarcoma." This cancer had been seen only in a tribe in central Africa and occasionally, for unknown reasons, in elderly Jewish and Italian men. Usually the disease appeared as purplish spots on the skin and wasn't especially dangerous. But now, all of a sudden, it was deadly. When some of the men also came down with pneumocystis, doctors were baffled. Then, when men in Los Angeles and San Francisco began reporting the very same symptoms, doctors were alarmed. Was this some new kind of superbug?

Adding to the mystery was a very strange detail: All of the men with this new disease were gay. But Dr. Rask had been a female, and she had died in Europe. What was going on? How had this illness gotten to the United States, and why was it targeting gay men?

Health officials interviewed the sick men and began backtracking in search of any kind of common link. They found one.

"I'm not about to slow down. I have too much living to do." Those were the words of a young gay flight attendant named Gaëtan Dugas when he was diagnosed with Kaposi's sarcoma. Based in Canada, Dugas flew to major cities around the world. And wherever he went, he had sex with numerous men. This was particularly true in large American cities. It's doubtful that

Dugas actually introduced this new disease to the United States, but he certainly spread it. And he spread it specifically among gay men.

By the end of 1981, 121 gay men had died from this strange illness, and a few hundred more had been diagnosed with it. Health officials came up with a name for what some had been calling "gay cancer" or "the gay plague": Gay-Related Immune Deficiency, or GRID.

It's hard to believe that a mysterious disease that had killed more than 100 Americans was almost completely ignored by the press, but it was. In 1980, most Americans were still uncomfortable with the idea of homosexuality. Many states still had laws that made it a crime to be gay. Most people wanted to pretend that gay people didn't really exist. So when the press heard that this illness killed gay men, it felt no one would care. No one would want to read a story about *that*.

"Of course, *we* knew about it," said a gay man in San Francisco years later. "We knew something terrible was happening. But, you know, the rest of the country acted like nothing was going on. And so, sad to say, there was way less caution than there should have been."

It was suspected that GRID was passed through sexual contact, but it hadn't been proven. So when health officials tried to shut down gay clubs and bathhouses where men often met and had sex, some gay people protested loudly. This seemed like an unfair, if not illegal, attack on gay rights. But others disagreed.

"Something we are doing is a ticking time bomb that is causing the breakdown of our immunity," one gay writer explained. "We don't know what it is, but isn't it better to be cautious?"

By July of 1982, three new cases of GRID were being reported every day. But by then the disease had also appeared among drug users who used needles to inject their drugs. And for some reason, people from Haiti had become victims. Additionally, GRID was occasionally traced to heterosexual prostitutes. Clearly, this was an illness spread through blood and sexual contact. It wasn't a gay disease—it was a human disease.

Health officials decided to change the names to AIDS, which stands for "Acquired Immune Deficiency Syndrome." And in August of 1982, AIDS was declared a national epidemic in the United States. Still, no one wanted to talk about this disease.

"Federal health officials call it an epidemic," Dan Rather finally said on the *CBS Evening News*. "Yet you rarely hear a thing about it."

It was the first time AIDS had been mentioned on television. Yet it had killed more than 1,000 people.

Most Americans didn't express much sympathy. Because the disease continued to be associated with gay people and sex, many considered it shameful and better left ignored.

And since no one talked about this epidemic, most Americans did not understand it. Few realized that AIDS did not recognize sexual orientation. It killed men, women, and children without preference. And it was not just a "gay American disease." In parts of Africa, AIDS was spreading at an alarming rate.

Making matters worse, President Ronald Reagan refused to speak about AIDS or support any kind of AIDS research. Many of Reagan's strongest supporters were very conservative. Perhaps Reagan was worried about losing political power if he showed concern for this "gay disease."

As a result, when doctors and scientists asked for federal funds for AIDS research, they were denied again and again. Meanwhile, doctors studying a small and short-lived epidemic known as "Legionnaire's Disease" received nearly $10 million in federal research funds. Legionnaire's Disease had killed barely 100 people, but many of its victims were important businessmen. Within the gay community, there was outrage.

"If this were a new form of cancer attacking straight people, it would be receiving constant media attention!" shouted one activist. "Government funding would be endless. For God's sake, our president would *talk* about it!"

By the mid-1980s the ignorance and fear surrounding AIDS produced an epidemic of their own. Even though doctors had proven that AIDS could be transmitted only through exchange of blood or through sexual contact, most people would not believe it. In San Francisco, jurors refused to sit in the same room with an AIDS patient. As during other epidemics, like the Black Death or yellow fever, some doctors flatly refused to care for victims. People were afraid to hug or even speak to those with AIDS. Some suggested that those with AIDS should be placed in isolation.

And some people physically or verbally attacked people with AIDS. That is what happened to Ryan White. Ryan was not gay, and it wasn't possible to "catch" AIDS from him through a drinking fountain or by sitting near him in the cafeteria. But ongoing ignorance about AIDS created panic and irrational fear. Ryan was treated so hatefully by his classmates and the people of Kokomo that he and his mother finally moved to a different town. However, Ryan's story upset and puzzled a lot of people. How could everyone treat a young person so cruelly? And how had Ryan gotten AIDS anyway?

Like a growing number of young AIDS victims, Ryan had a prior disease that required frequent blood transfusions. AIDS was an unusual disease in that it took a long time, sometimes years, to actually make a victim sick. As a result, many people donated blood, not realizing they had AIDS. When this blood was given to a patient, AIDS was passed along also.

Ryan's sad story—and other stories like his—finally got people talking. The media began presenting stories about infants who had contracted AIDS through blood transfusions. There was a particularly heartbreaking story about a five-year-old girl and her pregnant mother. Suddenly, there was a public outcry for what many called the "innocent victims." Why hadn't anything been done? Why weren't scientists and doctors being funded?

Although President Reagan still refused to speak about AIDS, Congress agreed to fund AIDS research. Scientists in both France and the United States worked quickly and tirelessly to try to find the cause of AIDS. In 1983, each group of scientists announced that they had discovered a virus that seemed to be the cause of AIDS. This virus was named HIV for "Human Immunodeficiency Virus" (meaning a virus that damages the immune system in humans, and keeps them from being able to fight disease in their body). Once the virus had been discovered, it was possible to test both people and blood for HIV. Next, scientists hoped to find drugs to slow the progress of the disease and, possibly, to find a vaccine to keep people from getting it.

This would prove to be terribly difficult.

Scientists knew that once the HIV virus enters the human body, it can take anywhere from a few months to more than ten years for people to develop symptoms of AIDS. But when AIDS finally does begin attacking the immune system, people may experience different symptoms. Some patients develop pneumocystis, while others get Kaposi's sarcoma. Sometimes AIDS attacks the brain or the spinal cord. Some victims go blind. For these reasons and more, scientists had a tough time fighting the disease. Treatments that worked for one patient might not work for another.

As doctors and scientists studied and researched this baffling disease, it claimed a most unexpected victim.

In the 1940s, a tall, handsome man named Roy Fitzgerald had decided to head to Los Angeles to see if he could have a career in the movies. He had been in the Navy and had worked as a truck driver, but he had always loved acting. It didn't take long for Roy to make it big. He was the perfect romantic leading man, and by the 1950s, he was one of Hollywood's biggest stars—going by the name Rock Hudson.

When Hudson became increasingly tired in 1984, he was worried. When he saw a purplish spot on his neck in 1985, he was scared. After being diagnosed with AIDS, he flew to Paris to try experimental AIDS treatments, but they didn't work. In July of 1985, it was announced that Rock Hudson was dying of AIDS. And although he had kept it hidden from the public during his forty-year career, just weeks before his death, news stories revealed that he was gay.

Knowing that Rock Hudson had AIDS caused many Americans to view both AIDS and its victims differently. It made them realize that anyone could get this dreaded disease. And anyone could be gay—even a much-loved movie star.

"I am not happy that I have AIDS," Hudson said a month before he died late in 1985. "But if that is helping others, I can at least know that my own misfortune has had some positive worth."

Although President Ronald Reagan had been a friend of Hudson's, he had no public comment to make about Hudson's death. And although Reagan described AIDS research as a top priority, he was still reluctant to say anything at all about a disease that, in the United States anyway, mostly attacked gay men. Like many Americans, President Reagan felt that silence was the most appropriate way to deal with this epidemic. It would be two more years before the president would finally talk about AIDS. By that point, there were more than 40,000 cases of AIDS in the United States. And it had killed more than 20,000 Americans.

In 1987, a group of six gay activists in New York City came up with the slogan "Silence = Death." Soon, posters with this phrase began appearing in cities across the United States. The message was clear: As long as Americans refused to talk about AIDS or face the fact that it was a dangerous epidemic, the disease would continue to become more dangerous. It was obvious that AIDS was spread through sexual contact, but many Americans were unwilling to talk about condoms or safe sex. It was desperately important for young people to understand the dangers of unprotected sex, but many people were against this kind of education. They felt it would only encourage minors to have sex.

Over the next several years, scientists and doctors worked quickly to develop drugs that could slow the attack of HIV and keep people from developing symptoms of AIDS. Because of their discoveries, more and more people carrying HIV are able to live for years. One of these people is basketball star Magic Johnson. Johnson stated that he probably contracted the virus through having unprotected sex with female prostitutes. He was only 32 years old at the time. In 1991, the same year Johnson was diagnosed, he formed the Magic Johnson Foundation. In addition to improving urban minority communities, the foundation helps to educate people about AIDS.

"I want to help educate *all* people about what this disease is about," Johnson said. "We should not discriminate against people who have AIDS and HIV."

So much progress has been made in the treatment of HIV that Magic Johnson claimed in 2009 that the only time he even remembers he has the virus is when he has to take his daily medication. Even so, Johnson is the first to point out that he is far from cured. He also stresses that his health is the exception, not the rule. AIDS is still exceedingly dangerous—and far too many people are still contracting it through unsafe sex.

It is estimated that more than one million Americans are living with HIV/AIDS today. Worldwide, the number of people living with HIV/AIDS is about 38 million—90 percent of them in Africa. Even decades after AIDS was discovered, many people, particularly in Africa, do not understand or believe how the disease is spread. Poverty and lack of healthcare only make matters worse. In some of the poorest parts of Africa, nearly 25 percent of the population is infected. Thirty years ago, no one would have believed that a strange and little-discussed illness wrongly named "gay cancer" would become one of the deadliest diseases known to humankind. So far, more than 30 million people in the world have died of AIDS-related diseases.

Only months before Ryan White died, he spoke honestly about what his life had been like since he had been diagnosed with AIDS several years earlier.

"I came face to face with death at thirteen years old," Ryan said. "That was tough enough, but then no one would speak to me. Even at church, no one would shake my hand. Fear, discrimination, and ignorance are terrible things. I hope that one day, some day, all that changes."

# The Fury of Rabies

Around midnight, bats began pouring out of a dark, damp cave along a mountain ridge. By the hundreds, they swooped and darted along the Amazon River in Peru. They were in search of prey. But their prey was not the typical insects and fruit that many kinds of bats seek. These were vampire bats, and they were looking for blood.

These eerie bats looked something like big-nosed, pointed-eared mice flying through the night sky. Their furry bodies were small—barely three inches in length. But their leathery and spiny wings spanned more than 8 inches. Needle-sharp tiny fangs hung over their black lips. These fangs would come in handy for piercing skin. And the vampire bats' small tongues would come in handy for quickly lapping up the dripping blood of their victims.

In search of a meal, some of the bats moved

toward a small nearby village. The villagers kept herds of goats and cattle, and these animals are a vampire bat's favorite blood dispensers. It is estimated that in one year, 50 bats can drink the blood of about 10 cows. However, a single meal of blood for a vampire bat is so small (around an ounce) that a goat or cow is not harmed. In fact, these bats are so light and their bites so small that many of their victims sleep right through the bloodsucking. After eating, the vampire bat rests for a while on its victim's neck or back, and then it flies back to its cave to sleep.

But 2008 had brought drought to this part of Peru, and it had hurt the herds of livestock in the village. By 2009, there was not enough blood for the bats. And if a vampire bat has to go for more than two nights in a row without drinking blood, it will usually die. Deprived of cow blood, some of the bats flew silently near the huts of the village. They could smell and sense warm-blooded animals asleep inside the huts. Humans are not typically on a vampire bat's menu, but tonight they were.

The bats drifted soundlessly through open windows. They landed lightly on their victims. For unknown reasons, the bats seemed particularly drawn to children. Perhaps it was because the children's hearts beat faster. The vampire bats used their sensitive noses to detect bare skin. Creeping along blankets, they found exposed arms, necks, and faces. The bats sunk their teeth into the children. Then, they lapped up blood for nearly 30 minutes. Not one child woke up.

The next morning, a few children noticed what looked like small scratches on their body, but no one thought anything of it. In one of the huts, an eight-year-old girl named Eva awoke to find a bat wobbling around on the floor of her room. Every now and then, it would lift into the air, fly strangely, and then drop back to the floor. Eva called her mother, who killed the bat and threw it out into the bushes behind their small home.

"I think it bit me," the little girl said nervously, pointing to a tiny mark on her hand.

"A bat that small can't hurt you," her mother said with a smile. "There's nothing to be afraid of."

"Then why did you kill it?" Eva asked.

"You saw how it was flying," her mother replied. "It must have had a broken wing. It was best to put it out of its misery."

And that was that. Life went on as usual for Eva and the other children who had been bitten. Then, about three months later, Eva felt a strange tingling in her hand right at the spot where the vampire bat had bitten her. Then she became sick with a headache and a fever. And Eva was not alone. Several other children in the village felt the same tingling and had the same illness. But it was certainly not unusual for children to share illnesses. No one was too concerned.

However, a week or so later, weird things began happening.

Eva became jumpy and often shouted out in terror for no clear reason. Every other night, dreams or visions would send her into a screaming panic. One night, Eva's father brought her a glass of water when he had finally gotten her calmed down. Eva looked at the glass and made a strangling sound. Her eyes grew big, and she scrambled out of her bed. As she cowered in a corner, she began drooling and crying. Then, just as suddenly, she seemed to return to normal. She couldn't understand why she was in the corner of her room. She fearfully refused the water, but she got back into bed and slept until morning.

Over the next several days, Eva's "normal" moments became fewer and fewer. By the end of the week, her parents had tied her hands and feet down to keep her from kicking, biting, and clawing herself. Her eyes rolled to the back of her head, and terrible convulsions arched her back painfully. A thick, foamy drool dribbled out of her mouth, and she shouted words that made no sense. One moment her skin would be hot to the touch. The next, Eva would be shivering uncontrollably. The sight or sound of water made her insane with fear.

The other sick children in the village had similar symptoms. No one could figure out what was happening. Had these children become possessed by an evil spirit? A week later, Eva went into a coma. One of the villagers made the long trip to a town where there was a hospital. Two days before Eva died, a doctor finally took a look at her. Right away, he thought he knew what was wrong.

"Was Eva recently bitten by a dog?" the doctor asked.

Her parents shook their heads.

"Maybe a wild animal?" he asked.

Still, no.

The parents sat in silence until the mother suddenly gasped. The bat! She had forgotten all about it. When she told the doctor she had killed it and thrown it out back, the doctor walked outside to collect what was left of the bat. He carefully placed it in a jar and took it with him to be examined in a lab. Even though the vampire bat was rotted, and barely resembled a bat anymore, scientists found clear traces of a deadly virus inside its crumbling skull—rabies.

Nearly 200 years earlier, a young boy living in a small town in France heard terrible screams one evening. Along with other townspeople, he hurried toward the shouts. He'd never forget what he saw next: A crazed wolf was circling around a mother and her two children. Foam dripped from the wolf's mouth, and its eyes bulged out of its head. Every few steps, the wolf would teeter sideways. It snarled and yapped loudly.

All at once, the wolf leaped at the woman, bit her on the face, and ran straight into the crowd. There was much confusion, scattering, and screaming, and the wolf bit several more people. The boy managed to steer clear of the wolf, but he watched it stagger through town, snapping and snarling at every human or animal it encountered.

Within a few months, the eight people and several animals that had been bitten by the wolf all died. This was no surprise to the townspeople. They had known right away that the wolf had rabies. But they also knew right away that there was nothing they could do about it. In fact, for thousands of years, people had been aware that a bite from a strange-acting animal could lead to death.

"Some dogs suffer from madness," wrote the famous Greek philosopher Aristotle in 400 B.C. "This causes them to become very irritable, and all animals they bite become diseased."

Many years later, it would be discovered that these "irritable" dogs were not mad; they were sick. In ancient times, however, it appeared that these dogs were insane. As a result, the dogs were said to have "rabies," which comes from *rabere*, the Latin word for "madness."

The little boy who'd witnessed the wolf with rabies grew up wondering why there was no cure for this disease. In fact, the boy wondered why there were no cures for a lot of diseases.

When he became a man, he dedicated his life to searching for answers. His name was Louis Pasteur. Today, we refer to "pasteurized" milk, because Pasteur discovered a method for making milk safe to drink. He developed vaccines for numerous animal diseases, making chicken, beef, and pork safer for people to eat. In addition, Pasteur developed a vaccine to protect humans from anthrax, a disease that was often spread to people from cattle or sheep.

So, by the time Louis Pasteur was in his sixties, he had accomplished a lot. Everyone expected him to retire and relax, especially since he had suffered a stroke that had left him partially paralyzed on the left side of his body. But Pasteur had never forgotten that rabid wolf. It still haunted his dreams at night. Pasteur had one last goal before he could be comfortable in retirement: He was determined to figure out what caused rabies and how he could keep people from getting it.

Pasteur knew that the rabies virus could be found in the saliva of rabid dogs. He sent word out to veterinarians and townspeople, asking them to let him know if they happened to see any rabid dogs running around. (Some of the townspeople sometimes wondered if Pasteur might be a little crazy himself.) Finally, he received word of a mad bulldog wandering around a nearby farm. Pasteur ordered his assistant to capture the dog and bring him into the lab. A stiff noose was placed around the dog's neck so that his bared teeth could not reach his captor. Next, Pasteur would somehow try to collect saliva out of the dog's mouth.

Pasteur found a long glass tube and walked slowly toward the growling dog. As his assistant struggled to hold the dog's neck still, Pasteur leaned close and slid the tube inside the dog's mouth. Then, quickly, Pasteur placed his own mouth on the other end of the tube and sucked up a bit of dog spit. He stopped sucking before the spit reached his own mouth, and he stuck his finger over the end of the tube. It was a courageous, and dangerous, way to collect the rabies virus. Pasteur later admitted to having shaky hands and a pounding heart when he finished.

Pasteur worked on his vaccine for a year. Although he felt fairly certain that it would work, it had been tested only on dogs. No one knew if it would actually prevent humans from getting rabies.

In July of 1885, Pasteur was in the process of doing some final testing when a nine-year-old boy and his parents showed up at the Pasteur lab. They had traveled by train to see him.

"A mad dog has bitten him," his mother explained desperately. "We have been told that you can cure him."

Pasteur shook his head. He explained that the vaccine wasn't quite ready.

"But you must try!" the father pleaded. "He

could die if you don't even try!"

The little boy, named Joseph Meister, looked very afraid. It was too soon for him to have any symptoms, but his face was pale with terror. Joseph looked into Pasteur's eyes and silently begged him to keep him from getting the awful disease.

Louis Pasteur had a very tough decision to make. After all, only about 15 percent of the people who were bitten by a rabid animal actually got rabies. Sometimes, not enough saliva reached the bloodstream. And occasionally, the reaction was no more than a slight fever. Sometimes, there was no reaction at all. What if the vaccine, not rabies, killed this little boy? Pasteur stayed up all night thinking about this. In the morning, however, he'd made up his mind: He would give the vaccine to Joseph.

The vaccine actually consisted of a series of shots—one a day for nearly two weeks. During these weeks, terrible nightmares haunted Pasteur's sleep. Visions of Joseph foaming at the mouth and howling made Pasteur wake up in a cold sweat. Several times, he dreamed of the rabid wolf he had seen when he was a child. In his dream, the wolf was chasing after him, his fangs dripping with blood.

Then, more than midway through the series of shots, a frightening accident occurred: One of Pasteur's assistants stumbled when carrying a prepared shot toward Joseph. The needle jabbed into the assistant's leg. Pasteur's vaccine was based on the commonly held theory that resistance to a virus is built up by exposing the body to stronger and stronger doses of that virus. Therefore, the assistant had just injected a rather strong dose of rabies virus deep into his leg.

The terrified assistant immediately asked to receive the full treatment. Then Pasteur had two patients to lose sleep over. But all his fears vanished when, two months later, neither Joseph nor the assistant showed any sign of the dreaded disease. Pasteur's rabies vaccine worked!

Joseph Meister was so grateful that he devoted his life to first helping Pasteur in his old age and then working as the gatekeeper of the Pasteur Institute after Pasteur died in 1895. In 1940, when Joseph was 60, Nazis stormed the Institute. They were intent on destroying it and defiling Pasteur's grave behind the building. Joseph did everything he could to keep them out. But when he realized that he could not block the invasion, he committed suicide. He could not bear to watch Nazis disgrace the grave of the man he honored so deeply.

"You must remember that there is no *cure* for rabies."

Again and again, Pasteur had reminded people of this fact. When word got out that Pasteur had perfected a vaccine, people from all over Europe began showing up at his door after they had been bitten by a rabid animal. They assumed the vaccine would save their lives. But the shots were effective only if they were received *before* the rabies virus began attacking the nervous system. And it was impossible to know when that would happen. Sometimes symptoms appeared just a few days after the person was bitten; other times they did not appear for more than a year. Sometimes, Pasteur began administering shots, only to watch a patient suddenly descend into madness.

Today, there is still no cure for rabies. And rabies is still a major problem. Worldwide, more than 55,000 people die horrible deaths every year after being bitten by a rabid animal (usually a dog). However, it is estimated that Pasteur's vaccine saves more than 300,000 lives annually. Still, a vaccine must be available in order for it to save a life. And in many parts of the world, like the remote area of Peru where the vampire bats attacked, there is very little medicine at all—much less a rabies vaccine.

After five children died from rabid bat bites in that small Peruvian village, doctors returned with a supply of vaccine. But they explained that doing everything to avoid bites in the first place is the best form of rabies prevention.

"We sleep with windows covered now," explained one villager. "It's hot sometimes, but it keeps the devil bats out."

So, what should *you* do if you're bitten by a wild animal? First of all, don't panic! Rabies is quite rare among wild animals. Chances are you have not been bitten by a rabid animal. Even so, you don't want to stake your life on that chance. You must follow a series of steps to ensure your health.

First, wash the bite area with soap and hot water for a full ten minutes. Next, call your doctor right away and tell her or him what happened. Your doctor can then decide the best way to proceed to prevent rabies or other infection. Remember that it takes at least a few days to a few months for rabies symptoms to appear. And if treatment is given before symptoms begin, you have no chance at all of getting rabies.

If it is possible to safely capture the animal that bit you, do so. However, don't take any risks! Call animal control officials to help you. If it can be determined that the animal does not have rabies, the doctor may do no more than give you an antibiotic for the bite. However, if the animal is rabid, you will need to undergo a series of five shots spread over fourteen days.

"The shots are not exactly fun," one doctor admitted. "But they're about one hundred percent more fun than getting a deadly disease."

# CHAPTER 7

## Mysteries Solved: Hidden Poisons at Home

When we think of where mysterious and deadly diseases lurk, we often think of dirty, crowded cities or primitive faraway places. Every winter, as the flu and other illnesses invade workplaces and schools, we breathe a sigh of relief when we're finally safe in our homes. But sometimes we're not quite as safe as we think. When we shut our doors and lock away the outside world, what are we locking inside with us? As the following three stories illustrate, mysterious illnesses don't always come from city streets or distant lands. Sometimes they're hiding right in our very own homes.

"Quick! I need help right away!" A panicked woman in Fresno, California, ran into an emergency room holding her eight-year-old son, Johnny. Johnny's skin was gray, and he was shaking all over. He cried out and clutched his stomach, and then he threw up. Next, his eyelids began fluttering as he passed out in his mother's arms.

Emergency staff rushed the boy to an examining room, where a doctor checked Johnny's pulse and temperature. The boy's heart was racing, and his body temperature was alarmingly high. When the doctor looked at Johnny's eyes, he noticed that the pupils were barely the size of pinpoints. When Johnny regained consciousness, he cried out about sharp pains in his stomach.

The doctor wasn't sure what was wrong. However, many of Johnny's symptoms seemed to indicate that he had been poisoned. More specifically, it appeared to be chemical poisoning, not food-related poisoning.

"Can you think of any chemicals that your son might have come in contact with?" the doctor asked.

Johnny's mother shook her head. Any chemicals in their home, like cleaners or bug sprays, were locked in a cabinet in the garage. Then she remembered something.

"Johnny told me that he had seen a crop-duster plane sitting in a field near his school this morning," his mother said. "He said that he and his friends went over to look at it."

The doctor nodded. It made sense. Crop-dusters often carried tanks of strong insecticides. These insecticides were diluted as they were sprayed into the air. But Johnny and his friends had played around the crop-duster plane. If Johnny had touched the plane where the insecticide sprayed out and then put his fingers in his mouth, he could easily have gotten a fairly strong dose of poison. The doctor took a sample of Johnny's blood and then gave him medicine that would counteract pesticide poisoning. By the next morning, Johnny was almost back to normal. And his blood tests came back showing that he had indeed been made sick from a strong pesticide. Case closed, right? Not so fast.

A few days later, the doctor received some puzzling news. After Johnny's run-in with the crop-duster near the school, the doctor had notified health officials. But word came back that the plane had been empty—it hadn't carried any bug spray in weeks. The doctor scratched his head. It didn't make sense. But Johnny was better, so it wasn't worth worrying about.

Then, the next morning, Johnny was back at the hospital with the very same symptoms he'd had the first time. What was going on? Where was this little boy going that put him in contact with deadly pesticides? The doctor questioned both Johnny (when he was feeling better) and his parents, but there were no clues at all. Finally, the doctor contacted health officials and asked them to look into this mystery.

After an exhausting day of research and questioning, the two men from the health department had come up with only one curious detail: Johnny's mother had recently bought her son five pairs of jeans from the salvage depot of a local trucking company. The salvage depot often sold merchandise that had been slightly damaged in transit and had been refused by the receiving stores.

"The jeans were half price because they were stained," Johnny's mother explained. "But I couldn't see a stain on any of them."

The curious detail was that Johnny had been wearing a pair of those jeans both times he had gotten ill. The health officials decided to do an experiment. Back at the health department's labs, one of the officials placed a pair of the jeans into a container that housed several dozen mosquitoes. Within five minutes, every insect was dead. Not only that, mosquitoes in containers twenty feet away began dying. The insecticide had been found! But how had it gotten onto the jeans?

It turned out that, against all kinds of laws and regulations, the jeans had been shipped in a truck that also carried seventy-two containers of an extremely poisonous insecticide. One of the containers had fallen over and spilled onto a stack of jeans. When the jeans arrived at the department store, they had been rejected because of what appeared to be oil stains. But by the time the jeans were returned to the salvage depot, the insecticide had dried up. No stain was visible, so the jeans were eagerly purchased. But the poison was just as dangerous when it was dry and invisible as it had been when it was wet.

Six other children in Fresno also got very sick when they wore the poisoned jeans. And, just like Johnny's parents, the parents of those children had racked their brains trying to figure out what on earth their children had been getting into on their way to school. The parents would never have guessed that their children were being made so ill by something they were getting into before they even left their bedrooms.

"We're just thankful that none of the children died," a doctor later commented. "The toxic level on some of those jeans was unbelievable."

As for the trucking company, it tried to defend itself by claiming that items sold at salvage depots were "as is." In addition, they argued that anyone should know to wash "rejected" clothing before wearing it. The judge didn't buy it. The company was fined $10,000.

"What is wrong with all of us?" Tom McDevitt said, looking at his family sitting gloomily around the dinner table. "Maybe it's time to go to the doctor."

Tom and his wife, Brenda, had barely touched their food. For nearly two months, Tom had felt tired, and his head ached now and then. Sometimes his stomach hurt, but the pain never seemed severe enough for him to visit the doctor.

"Maybe we all just have a touch of the flu," Brenda suggested. "I guess we should feel lucky not to have gotten the full flu!"

But Tom wasn't so sure. A "touch" of something shouldn't last this long. And there was something else that seemed strange: His two older children, four-year-old Sean and three-year-old Margie, had also felt sick, but the six-month-old baby seemed to be feeling fine. She ate and laughed and looked around the table, demanding attention from her sluggish family.

Another week went by, and none of the McDevitts seemed to feel any better—but they also felt no worse. Perhaps, Tom thought, spring weather would cheer them up. In the meantime, Tom and Brenda worked to plan a birthday party for Sean. But Sean, usually thrilled with even the mention of cake and ice cream, didn't really seem to care about his upcoming party. When his parents reminded him that there would games, presents, and even a clown, he just shrugged.

On the afternoon of the party, Sean seemed withdrawn and irritable. He didn't feel like eating, and he even tossed a plate of food at his best friend. Later, after the miserable party ended, Sean began running a fever and threw up. When Tom quietly entered his son's room to check on him that night, Sean woke up and began crying.

"I feel funny," he complained to his father.

"Funny how?"

"My arm doesn't move," Sean said. "And my leg feels funny, too."

In alarm, Tom threw back the covers and looked at his son. Checking more closely, Tom realized that the entire left side of Sean's body was paralyzed. Immediately, Tom rushed his son to the hospital. After a number of tests, the doctor shook his head in some bewilderment.

"We can't figure out why he's paralyzed," the doctor said, "but the tests show that your son is extremely anemic and also malnourished."

Tom was stunned. How could this be? Anemia (weakness caused by a lack of oxygen-carrying cells in the blood) and malnourishment were often signs of child neglect. But Tom and his wife fed their children very well and made sure they took vitamins. In embarrassment and worry, Tom asked the doctor how this was possible. The doctor didn't know, but he suggested that Sean remain at the hospital for a while so that he could be observed. During this time, Sean would receive a blood transfusion to help combat the anemia.

Within a week, Sean was back to normal. His paralysis suddenly disappeared, and, just as suddenly, his appetite returned. He couldn't wait to go back home and play with the birthday toys he had been too sick to enjoy. Sean's sister Margie, however, was almost too sick to stay awake at the dinner table. Sometimes, Tom found his daughter sitting alone in a room crying and holding her stomach. When he took her to the doctor, still believing that it was nothing more than the flu, Tom was once again shocked to hear that his daughter also appeared to be anemic and malnourished.

What was going on? The doctor recommended that Tom have his own blood tested. When Tom's blood test showed the same result, the doctor looked very concerned.

"I don't want to frighten you," the doctor said carefully, "but it looks as though your family is being poisoned."

"Poisoned?" Tom asked with a dismayed expression. "How?"

"I don't know how," the doctor answered. "But it looks like lead poisoning. You need to check your home very carefully. Perhaps there's a high level of lead in your water pipes. Or there may be lead in paint that's somehow getting ingested."

But all of Tom's searching led to dead ends. The pipes were fine, and there was no peeling lead-based paint anywhere in the house. But as Tom and Brenda continued searching, everyone in the family except the baby continued getting sicker and sicker.

"Get out of your house," a close friend finally warned. "It may be the only way to save your lives."

However, since Tom had no idea what was poisoning his family, he worried that they might very well unknowingly pack up the poison and move it with them. He felt as though they were living in a terrifying nightmare.

Then one morning, Tom sat at breakfast, bleary-eyed and exhausted, watching Brenda pour orange juice into the glasses on the table. Suddenly, Tom realized something that made him sit up and open his eyes wide: Everyone drank orange juice except the baby! And every day for the past few months, the juice had been stored in a beautiful ceramic pitcher that Brenda had received as a Christmas gift. The pitcher had been handmade in Mexico. The pieces of the puzzle quickly began falling into place as Tom remembered once reading something about glazes used on pottery. Some glazes could be very toxic if they were not diluted before they were used.

"Stop!" Tom ordered. "Don't drink the juice. I think I've figured it out."

Later that afternoon, the mystery was finally solved. A health official who had tested the pitcher visited Tom and handed him a small bag of white powder. "This is a chemical known as pure lead chromate," the official said. "It came out of your pitcher when we washed it with acid. There's enough here to kill two people."

Following this scare, Tom McDevitt worked with others to get the Food and Drug

Administration (FDA) to set limits on the amount of lead that could be used in ceramic products. However, these limits still do not apply to a number of countries, including Mexico.

"Just be careful—and aware that some ceramics can be dangerous," an FDA official advised. "No one ever expects poison to be that pretty."

Ten-year-old Shawn Jones was bored. It was the middle of February, and the snow was coming down so hard that he couldn't see even the big oak tree in his backyard. All morning he had begged his mother to let him go out in the snow, but his mother had refused. Now Shawn lay back on his bed, trying to think of a good reason to go outside. It would have to be something that disguised the fact that he really just wanted to play in the snow. As Shawn thought, his cat, Fluffy, jumped up on his stomach and began purring. Shawn petted her, and even kissed her on her head. Fluffy had been around as long as Shawn had been alive, and the two of them had an unusual bond.

"That's *it*!" Shawn suddenly said out loud, startling his cat. He looked at her and smiled. "I mean, what if you have to . . . well, you know."

Shawn jumped up and ran into the kitchen.

"Mom, don't you think it might be a good idea for me to shovel off a little trail so that Fluffy can get to the beach?"

"The beach" was the name the family gave to a sandy patch of ground in the backyard where Fluffy went to do her business. Shawn's mother didn't like having a cat box in the house, and Fluffy liked getting outside a few times a day. It was a situation that worked for everyone. But now a foot of snow covered the yard and the beach.

"She'll be okay without a trail, Shawn," Mrs. Jones replied. "She's made it through snow before."

"But I could shovel off the sidewalk, too, while I'm outside," Shawn said hopefully.

His mother sighed and smiled in spite of herself. "All right," she said. "But only for a little while. It's too cold and wet to be out there very long. And don't make a huge mess when you come back in."

Within five minutes, Shawn was bundled up and rushing out the back door. There was probably more snowball making than shoveling, but Shawn managed to make an admirable trail for his cat. However, as he wandered back toward the house, a sudden blast of pain in his head nearly made him pass out. Shawn threw down the shovel and grasped his head. All at once, he was having trouble breathing, and then his vision became blurred. As he struggled to the back door, the house seemed to swim in front of him. He barely got inside before he collapsed, crying out "Mom!" just once.

Shawn's mother called back from the kitchen, "I'm in here. What?"

But there was silence. When Mrs. Jones called to her son two more times and got no answer, she walked to the back door and saw him sprawled unconscious on the floor. Immediately, she shouted upstairs for her husband and dialed 911. Within ten minutes, an ambulance was rushing Shawn and his parents to a nearby hospital, where Shawn was hurried into the emergency room.

"I'm not sure what's wrong," the ER doctor admitted after examining Shawn. "But I have to tell you that your son's symptoms indicate some sort of serious trauma to either his brain or his left eye."

By that time, Shawn was awake, but the pain continued to throb in his head. When asked questions, he could respond only by shaking his head "no" to each one. Had he fallen outside? Had something jabbed his eye? Did something hit him in the head? Had he had some sort of accident recently?

Most troubling to the doctor was the appearance of Shawn's left eye. The pupil was so dilated that the colored part of his eye was nearly black except for a bloodshot ring around it. It was so gruesome to see that Shawn's mother had to look away every time her son turned to her. This, of course, frightened Shawn even more.

"We need to keep Shawn here," the doctor said in a low voice. "It's quite possible that we may need to do exploratory neurosurgery."

"*Brain surgery*?" Shawn's father asked in shock. "Are you sure?"

It was impossible to believe. Only an hour earlier, the Joneses' son had been outside throwing snowballs at the oak tree in their backyard. Now he was hooked up to all sorts of monitors, machines, and fluids. His condition was described as critical. It was heartbreaking.

Later that afternoon, the doctor sat alone in his office looking at Shawn's chart. So many things just didn't add up. When the reflexes of Shawn's eyes were checked, both seemed to be normal. So it didn't seem likely that he had severely injured his left eye. And there didn't appear to be any swelling or pressure behind Shawn's eye, so now a brain hemorrhage had also been ruled out. Except for his lingering headache, Shawn *seemed* healthy. He had even asked for a milkshake.

Then, like a misty, faraway memory of a dream, the doctor remembered something from an article he had read years earlier. Sometimes, particularly in children, a chemical in eye drops can cause a severe reaction. The reaction imitates eye or brain trauma, but very little, if any, real damage is ever done. After a day or so, the eye clears up, and everything returns to normal.

The doctor immediately rushed to Shawn's

room where Shawn's parents were still comforting their son.

"Is anyone in your family using eye drops?" the doctor asked.

This seemed like a strange question. Mr. and Mrs. Jones looked at each other and shook their heads.

"Has anyone, anyone at all, been in your house using any kind of eye drops?" the doctor asked again. "Are you positive?"

When the doctor explained how some people can react to certain eye medicines, the Joneses looked relieved and hopeful. But there were no eye drops in the house. And no one had visited since Christmas. There was a long silence in the room. Then, suddenly, Mrs. Jones clapped her hands.

"Fluffy! Oh my gosh! It's Fluffy!"

The doctor looked at Mrs. Jones with a blank expression.

"Fluffy?" he asked. "*What's* fluffy?"

"Fluffy. She's our cat. I had totally forgotten. She just got a prescription yesterday for drops for an eye infection."

The doctor then asked Shawn if he had petted or touched the cat at any time that morning. Shawn looked a little sheepish when he nodded and added, "I kissed her head, too."

That night, Shawn was back home, and his headache was gone. His eye was nearly back to normal. Shawn was not allowed to touch Fluffy, but before he went to bed, he looked at her curled up in her favorite chair by a heat vent.

"A lot of thanks I get from *you* for clearing you a path in the snow," he said with a grin. "Spoiled cat."

## CHAPTER 8

# Creepy Invaders

No one likes to think about it, but we all have "bugs" in our body. Living bacteria swarm our guts. In fact, it's estimated that most people carry around about 100 *trillion* microscopic bugs, mostly in the stomach and intestines. Some of us even have very tiny worms that float around harmlessly in our digestive systems. The good news is that most bacterial bugs in the human body are helpful. They break down foods, clear away toxins, and keep a balance of digestive acids.

The bad news, of course, is that some bugs and worms are dangerous parasites. In their search for human blood, some bugs (crawling ones, not bacterial ones) bite us and send toxins into our system. And a host of unwelcome worms view the human body as both a home and an endless source of food. These creepy invaders can make us very sick—some can even kill us.

• • •

"Listen to my voice," Danielle Jordan said shakily to her husband over the phone. "Do I sound like there's something wrong with me?"

"What do you mean?" her husband, Mark, asked.

"Words," was all Danielle could manage to say for several seconds. "I keep losing words."

Danielle's morning had been like any other morning. Then, as she was speaking with a client, she seemed to lose the ability to talk correctly. Parts of the words she was trying to say kept getting chopped off. Try as she might, she couldn't remember how to speak. Terrified, she had called her husband. But now her speech was beginning to come back.

"I think you just had too much coffee this morning," Mark said with a laugh. "You sound okay to me."

But Danielle wasn't okay. Three hours later, her speech began halting and slurring again. Then it completely broke down into what sounded like baby talk. When the left side of her face began twitching and went numb, Danielle thought she was having a stroke.

*Call my husband*, she managed to scribble on a piece of paper for a co-worker to read.

But by the time Mark had rushed his wife to the hospital, she seemed to be fine again. When the doctor examined Danielle, she couldn't find anything obviously wrong. Danielle hadn't had a stroke, and though her symptoms were similar to those of someone suffering from a migraine headache, Danielle had no pain in her head.

The doctor was troubled by the fact that Danielle had had two bouts of speech loss only a few hours apart. And the left side of Danielle's face was drooping slightly. These symptoms made the doctor suspect that there might be something wrong with Danielle's brain. She recommended several scans and x-rays.

The pictures were alarming.

"I see a small dark spot on your brain," the doctor explained. "I don't know exactly what it is yet, but it's on the surface of the left side near the part of the brain that controls speech."

Danielle was shocked.

"What do you think it is?" Danielle asked hesitantly.

The doctor paused. Then she said, "There's a fairly good chance that it's a tumor. However, we won't know if it's a dangerous tumor until we take a tiny biopsy of it."

Danielle could not believe it. How could this be happening? She sought out second and third opinions, but the other doctors agreed that it looked like a tumor. One doctor even told Danielle that, based on the size of the tumor, she probably had only a fifty-fifty chance of being alive in three years. In desperation, Danielle asked for more opinions from more neurosurgeons. All of the doctors seemed to agree, regardless of how much Danielle wanted to hear something else.

Then late one night, about a week later, Danielle received a phone call from a doctor at the University of California.

"I don't see a tumor when I look at these scans," he told her. "I see a worm."

A *worm?* On her brain? Danielle asked how this was possible.

The doctor explained that worm larva cysts are sometimes found in pork. If the pork is not cooked completely, these small cysts are swallowed, and the still-live larvae are released into the human intestine. There a pork tapeworm that can grow up to three feet long settles in for up to *ten years!* During those years, the tapeworm can release up to 30,000 eggs per day. The eggs are passed from the body with other waste from the intestine. And if hands are not washed thoroughly, the eggs can be passed on to someone else.

If a person eats a tapeworm egg (which is smaller than a pinhead), a worm called a "cysticercus" hatches in the human stomach. It is then carried by the bloodstream to the place where it will settle—usually in the eye or the brain, or in muscle tissue. There, it will live for years, feeding on the blood of its host and resting in a small hole that it burrows. People who have ingested multiple cysticerci may have numerous holes in their brain. In time, this can lead to seizures, terrible pain, and then death.

But Danielle was lucky. Her scans showed

only one hole. And a few doses of medicine would kill the worm.

"How long do you think I've had this worm?" Danielle asked.

When the doctor said that the worm had probably been in her brain for about six years, Danielle asked why she was only being bothered by it now.

"Because it's dying," the doctor explained. "As long as the worm is healthy, it releases a chemical that keeps the brain from reacting to its presence. But as soon as the worm begins dying, the area around the worm grows inflamed. That's what's happening in your brain."

"But if the worm is dying," Danielle asked, "Why do I need medicine to kill it?"

The doctor explained that it was very rare to ingest only one egg. Danielle probably had other cysticerci in her body. They were, perhaps, living in her muscles. Given time, they could create other problems.

Danielle was not thrilled with the idea of having a worm in her brain, but that was certainly preferable to having a deadly tumor. Danielle wondered where she had picked up the worm. It was very uncommon in most of North America, though it posed a serious problem in many parts of Mexico and South America. The doctor wondered if she had traveled to Mexico. And if so, had she eaten any raw fruits or vegetables?

Danielle and her husband had, in fact, visited Puerto Vallarta, Mexico, years earlier. But how could she possibly remember what she had eaten? Mark leafed through an old journal he used to keep during their travels. And there was the answer on page 42: *Beautiful evening last night! We had dinner overlooking the beach. We both had grilled fish, and, against her better judgment, Danielle ate the small salad. However, she seems fine today.*

Who would have guessed that it would take six years to feel the ill effects of that small salad?

In the mid-sixties, a woman in Lyme, Connecticut, named Polly Murray went out for a long walk in the woods on a beautiful late spring day. It had been a brutally cold and snowy winter, so the occasional buzzing of mosquitoes and gnats was almost a welcome annoyance. Polly wasn't even particularly bothered when she noticed two small bug bites under the collar of her shirt. She was just glad that summer was on its way.

A few weeks after her walk, Polly came down with what seemed to be the flu. She couldn't figure out why she had caught the flu in June, but she had all the symptoms: fever, headaches, and fatigue. One symptom seemed weird though.

"I had the strangest rashes," Polly recalled. "Each one of them looked almost like a bull's-eye on a dartboard."

That summer marked the beginning of years of poor health for Polly Murray. As soon as she would get well from one illness, she seemed to catch another. Her doctor diagnosed her first with the flu, and then with migraine headaches. When her joints began aching and swelling, she was diagnosed with arthritis and rheumatic fever. All of this was completely perplexing to Polly, since she had always been so healthy.

Then, about six years after Polly's illnesses began, her husband and four children began having the very same symptoms.

"I was convinced that everyone in the family had the same thing," Polly said. "It seemed so obvious. But the doctors refused to believe that our problems were related."

Polly decided to investigate a bit. She began asking neighbors if they had had any of these same symptoms. To her surprise, many had also been suffering from headaches, joint pain, and rashes. Children in more than a dozen families had complained about lingering aches that just never seemed to go away.

"I was really worried then," Polly admitted. "I wondered if something in the well water was making us sick. A nuclear power plant was just up the road. Were we all being poisoned by radioactivity?"

The next year, two of Polly's children were diagnosed with juvenile rheumatoid arthritis (JRA). This was a fairly rare disease, but at least it explained their achy joints—or did it? When Polly took her children to a special clinic at nearby Yale University, she was surprised to find out that an unusual number of children in Lyme had been diagnosed with JRA.

"I began asking around again, and discovered that there were 35 cases of JRA in Lyme," Polly said. "This was over *one hundred* times the normal rate! Something was wrong. Very wrong."

When Polly took her findings to officials at the Connecticut State Health Department, they agreed that something strange was happening. Two health officials began an investigation. They started by trying to find something that all the supposed victims of JRA might have in common.

"Food, water, other diseases, and even pets—we looked at everything. But nothing clicked," one official said.

Finally, the two investigators settled on three clues. All of the sick young people had initially developed the strange bull's-eye rash, they all lived near heavily-wooded areas, and they all had gotten their first symptoms in late spring or summer. Could the illness be connected to an insect bite?

Three months later, the officials found the guilty invader—the incredibly tiny deer tick. Because this tick is smaller than a pinhead, no one who had gotten sick even realized that he or she had been bitten by a tick.

"We were asked early on if we had pulled any ticks off our bodies," one victim said. "But everyone said no. These ticks are really hard to see!"

The Centers for Disease Control then entered the investigation. Disease spread by ticks, the eight-legged cousins of spiders and scorpions, was nothing new. When ticks feed on human blood, they suck blood in and spit saliva back out. If this saliva has bacteria or a virus in it, the tick's victim can become sick. But before doctors could determine how to treat this disease, they had to determine whether the disease was caused by a virus or a bacterium.

Several of the young people in Lyme were given doses of penicillin. Penicillin will kill many forms of bacteria, but it has no effect on viruses. Luckily, many of the victims who had been bitten more recently responded well to penicillin; nearly all of their symptoms disappeared. This was very good news, and a step in the right direction. However, Lyme disease, as it came to be named, would remain a puzzle for doctors and scientists. Where had this disease come from? And why did penicillin not help those, like Polly Murray, who had had the disease for a long time?

Today, Lyme disease continues to be a threat in the United States. Because it mimics other illnesses like the flu, strep throat, and even multiple sclerosis, Lyme disease has been nicknamed "the great imitator." These imitations make Lyme disease very hard for doctors to diagnose. Sometimes it can take years for either the doctor or the patient to pinpoint the illness. By the time the disease is diagnosed, it may be too late for effective treatment, and Lyme disease may plague its victim for the rest of his or her life.

"This is a tricky disease on so many levels," a doctor at the Centers for Disease Control said in 2005. "Prevention is your best protection. Wear clothes that cover you up when in tick-infested areas. Use an insect repellent with DEET in it. Check yourself closely for ticks immediately after being in the woods. All of this can help, but the only proven way you can absolutely avoid ticks is by staying inside all the time. Obviously, most people don't want to do that."

Here's something that sounds like it's straight out of a gruesome nightmare: Imagine a half-inch-long worm that spends its life cruising around your body. It digs holes, spreads infection, and generally just makes you feel awful. The worm is restless and keeps moving because it doesn't like being in the human body. It would prefer living inside a *snake*.

Finally, when the worm grows tired of looking for snakelike muscle tissue inside a creature that has none, it tunnels through muscle to get to skin. Once there, it creates a cyst and rests for a while. When the worm is sufficiently rested, it returns to its endless journey. It tunnels all through the body and even hitches a ride through the digestive system now and then. Most worms would be in danger of being passed out of the body at this point, but not this one. Four little hooks around its head grasp the walls of the intestine. There, it holds on until it begins digging again.

The restless journey of this little worm, called a *Gnathostoma*, can continue for more than twelve years! During that time, it can seriously weaken its human host. In the most severe (and rare) cases, this worm gets lost inside the human brain and tunnels frantically in search of skin to nap in. Even after the unfortunate host has died, the *Gnathostoma* travels on.

But how on earth does a snake-loving worm end up inside a human? Luckily, the process is rare.

In spring of 1999, a young Vietnamese-American man named Hahn began experiencing many unusual ailments. He got hives on his feet. He felt a terribly painful and sudden pressure on his liver. He was burning up one second and freezing the next. And every now and then, Hahn noticed an odd reddish cyst on his arms and legs.

Hahn's doctor checked his blood and noticed that the count for a certain type of white blood cell was extraordinarily high. This was the white blood cell that attacks invaders that enter the human body. Everyday intruders, like pollen or cat hair, are easily handled by about 300 of these cells per milliliter of blood. But Hahn's test showed an astounding 13,000 per milliliter! Immediately, Hahn's doctor suspected parasites.

"Hahn, have you recently traveled anywhere?" the doctor asked, trying to narrow down what might be in her patient's body.

"Just to Vietnam like I do every year," Hahn said.

Hahn had returned to his home every summer for several years. His resistance to many of the illnesses that affect Westerners was high. He had lived in Vietnam for most of his life, and his body was used to the exotic foods that his family served when he was home. The doctor wondered if Hahn had contracted malaria through a mosquito bite. But tests came back negative.

"Is there anything you can think of that was unusual or different about your visit?" the doctor persisted. "Maybe something odd you ate?"

At this question, Hahn thought for a while and then grinned.

"Well, it was kind of on a dare from my cousin," he said. "I ate half a cobra."

"A cobra!" The doctor looked both amazed and disgusted. "Why?"

"It's supposed to make you strong," Hahn said with a shrug. "And, anyway, my brother had eaten one last year. It was my turn."

When Hahn explained that the cobra was well-cooked, the doctor was relieved. A *Gnathostoma* would not survive in a cooked snake.

"But the cobra's heart was raw," Hahn mentioned, almost as an afterthought. "And as the guest of honor, I had to eat it."

"How did it taste?" the doctor couldn't help asking.

"Actually, pretty terrible," Hahn said with a smile.

The doctor guessed that it was the less-than-delicious cobra heart that had carried the worm into Hahn's body. Luckily, if this was a *Gnathostoma*, it had been traveling through Hahn for less than a year. Not too much damage could have been done. But was this the worm the doctor thought it was? Two days after his visit to the doctor, Hahn developed a cyst on his arm. This was a chance to catch the worm.

"If you'll agree to it," the doctor said, "we can surgically remove the cyst and, hopefully, get rid of your worm without having to do testing and prescribe drugs."

Hahn quickly agreed. But when the cyst was opened, there was no trace of the worm. The doctor used a microscope to see if any bit of the intruder had been left behind—hooks, fragments, intestines—but the entire worm had escaped back into Hahn's body. Now the doctor had no choice but to send a sample of Hahn's blood off for testing. She had to make absolutely sure he was carrying around a *Gnathostoma* before she could prescribe the drugs to kill it. And because there is no testing for this worm in the United States, Hahn's blood had to be sent all the way to Bangkok, Thailand.

A few stressful weeks later, the results finally came back. The doctor's hunch had been right. Now Hahn could take the drugs that would kill this worm once and for all. Within a month, all of Hahn's symptoms were gone, and he never had another cyst again.

"I still eat the same foods when I go home," Hahn later told his doctor. "But raw cobra heart is off the menu. I don't care how big the dare is."

CHAPTER 9

# The Invisible Killer

In the 1920s, Americans were car crazy. The automobile was a new and exciting invention, and suddenly everyone wanted one. For a while, some people argued that horse-drawn carriages were better than cars. A horse didn't get flat tires, and (at least in the early days of cars) a horse could move faster than many cars. Furthermore, horses didn't require gasoline.

One newspaper writer described this new fuel—gasoline—as "a filthy, evil-smelling substance that emits choking clouds when burned." The writer followed up by saying, "I'd choose a horse any day."

But that writer was far outnumbered by those who were thrilled by the shiny new Packard, Cadillac, and Model T cars. Who cared if these amazing machines used fuel that didn't smell like roses? After all, a horse was not exactly odor-free either.

At first, scientists and doctors worried about the effects of the poisonous lead that was added to gasoline. It was known to be harmful to humans. But in 1926, after a quick study by the federal government, leaded gasoline was declared to be "no danger" to people. Those who worked at gas stations or in the oil industry were advised to take extra precautions to keep their exposure to leaded gasoline low, however. As for the general public, the federal panel simply gave a vague warning: Gasoline may become "a menace to the health of the general public after prolonged use or under other conditions not now foreseen."

In other words, people could continue their use of leaded gasoline, and postpone their concern about safety until problems arose.

But many people in the areas of medicine and science *were* worried. In particular, they were concerned about the chemicals that were released in engine exhaust when gasoline was burned. Two chemicals, carbon dioxide ($CO_2$) and carbon monoxide (CO), filled the air when a car's engine used gasoline.

Carbon dioxide is not usually dangerous to humans. In fact, $CO_2$ is the chemical compound that we exhale after inhaling oxygen. Only in very rare cases have people been killed by $CO_2$. Just by chance, one of these cases happened right around the time that scientists were concerned about the chemicals in gasoline exhaust.

The frozen form of carbon dioxide, called "dry ice," can be dangerous if it melts in a small space where there is little air flow. Obviously, people do not often shut themselves away in airtight rooms with many pounds of dry ice, so no one really knew just how dangerous it could be.

However, on a ship bound for Brooklyn, New York, in the mid-1920s, six sailors found out what too much $CO_2$ can do. In the ship's cargo hold were thousands of pounds of fresh fruit. To keep the fruit cold, hundreds of pounds of dry ice were stacked against the walls. It was late summer, and the sailors' sleeping chambers were hot and uncomfortable. One particularly stifling night, half a dozen men decided to sling their hammocks in the chilly cargo hold.

The next morning, all of the men were dead. At first, no one could figure out what had happened. There was not a drop of blood anywhere, and there was no sign of a struggle or a fight. In fact, the dead sailors looked fairly peaceful in their hammocks. Had they frozen to death? That seemed unlikely, since most of the dry ice had evaporated back into the air overnight. It wasn't until an autopsy was performed that the mystery was solved. The men's blood was filled with carbon dioxide. When the ice "melted" and returned to a gas instead of a solid, it crowded all the oxygen out of the cargo hold. The sleeping men had never smelled it or felt a thing. They simply had never woken up.

"This brings up a very interesting possibility for a method of murder," one writer mused, "because it leaves no trace."

But scientists and doctors were not particularly concerned about a sudden increase of dry-ice murders. Their greater concern was the other much more deadly chemical in car exhaust: carbon monoxide. It didn't take long to figure out how lethal car exhaust could be. After a few incidents of people leaving their cars running in a closed garage, the danger was clear. It was estimated that the fumes from even a small car could kill a perfectly healthy person in about eight minutes. Auto exhaust from leaded gasoline contained up to 25 percent carbon monoxide, making it a very potent poison.

Around this same time, a similar type of gasoline was developed for stoves, lights, and furnaces in homes. No longer would people have to burn wood or coal, or light candles. This new gas seemed perfect. It was clean and nearly odorless, and it could be pumped into homes through pipes and tubes in the walls. What could go wrong? Well, a lot actually.

This new gas, known as illuminating gas, did not create a poisonous exhaust, but the invisible and odorless fumes from the gas were deadly. If a stove or light was working properly, the gas came in contact with a flame. Once the gas was ignited, it burned away and wasn't dangerous. But if there was a leak in a pipe, or if the pilot light had somehow gone out, gas fumes continued to pump into a home unchecked. And this gas had nearly twice as much carbon monoxide as car exhaust.

What makes CO so toxic? Think of carbon monoxide as a bully that hates oxygen. Obviously, humans need oxygen to live. Luckily, our blood contains iron, and oxygen is very attracted to iron. When we breathe in, the oxygen in the air rushes to attach itself to our red blood cells, and the two work together to keep us alive. Unfortunately, carbon monoxide is roughly 200 times more attracted to the iron in our blood than oxygen is. It doesn't want oxygen hogging all the iron, so it pushes it out of the way. Before long, carbon monoxide is completely in charge. Oxygen is denied entrance, and we die.

Someone who is beginning to be poisoned by carbon monoxide usually feels very tired. Then dizziness and confusion follow. The person may stumble around, and his or her talk may sound like nonsense. These symptoms originally led doctors to mistakenly believe that their patients were either drunk or mentally ill. Often, the patient was simply sent home and told to rest. But if the poisoning was the result of a slow leak in a gas pipe in the home, these doctors' orders were a prescription for death. The majority of carbon monoxide victims were found dead in their beds.

Still, the popularity of cars and the convenience of gas-powered lighting and appliances grew quickly in the 1920s. Before long, deaths due to carbon monoxide poisoning were skyrocketing. In 1925 in New York City alone, more than 1,000 people died from inhaling exhaust or gas fumes. Many of these deaths were accidental, but nearly one third of them were suicides.

"It's the easy way out," one police officer explained. "No pain, no mess. Just turn up the gas or seal up your garage, and close your eyes."

But some law enforcement officials were not so sure about all of those suicides or even all of the accidents. If it was so easy to die from CO poisoning, how easy might it be to murder someone with carbon monoxide and make it look like either a suicide or an accident? After all, it didn't take much work to make sure someone was asleep and then turn up the gas on a stove, blow out the pilot light, and place a teakettle over the unlit burner. Investigators would see the death as nothing more than an unfortunate mishap: Someone fell asleep while boiling water; the water put out the flame; the gas filled the room. As police began looking further into these "accidents," they uncovered an increasing number of murderous plots.

On the other hand, some murders were made to look like accidental CO poisoning when, in fact, the cause of death was something else altogether. In 1925, a desperate and unemployed man named Harry took out a $1,000 life insurance policy on his wife, Leah. Then, as she lay sleeping one morning, Harry put a pillow over her face and smothered her. In order to cover up his crime, Harry wrenched apart a light in the bedroom until he heard the hiss of gas. He'd had to fix that light several times in the past. It would simply look as though it had broken once again.

Not long after Harry ran out the back door, his young son went into his parents' bedroom to ask his mother a question. When the boy's mother wouldn't wake up, he tearfully ran to get a neighbor. The neighbor rushed over to check on the boy's mother. Because the room was dark and the light was broken, the neighbor lit a candle to get a closer look. Leah was cold and pale—definitely dead.

At first, police thought this was yet another carbon monoxide poisoning. But when they reviewed the details of the case, too many things didn't add up: If the woman had died as a result of gas coming out of the fixture, why hadn't her husband even gotten sick? And if the room had been so full of gas that it killed a grown woman, why hadn't there been an explosion when the neighbor lit the candle in the bedroom?

At the city morgue, doctors uncovered the most important detail when they pulled back the sheet from Leah's face. In cases of CO poisoning, the skin maintains an eerie and unsettling rosy glow long after death. This is because carbon monoxide changes the color of blood from a dark reddish blue (our blood is mostly blue until it is exposed to oxygen in the air) to an unnaturally brilliant pinkish cherry tone. This blood flushes the face and saturates both the brain and the lungs of CO victims. But Leah's face was as white as the sheet that had covered her.

When doctors examined Leah more closely, they saw finger-shaped bruises on her neck. When they tested her blood, there was not a trace of carbon monoxide in it. Harry was behind bars before nightfall.

Two years later, three thugs hooked one end of a rubber hose up to a gas lamp and shoved the other end into the mouth of a "friend" named Mike. Mike was a poor alcoholic who had been persuaded, in a moment of drunkenness, to sign over a life insurance policy to these men. The men knew that the sooner Mike died, the sooner they'd get his money.

On a Saturday night, the thugs had taken Mike out and told him they would buy him all the whiskey he could drink. Mike got so drunk that he passed out cold. The men then made a big show of carrying their drunken pal up the stairs to his room in a cheap boarding house. They pretended to be deeply concerned about his welfare.

"Is he sick?" the landlady asked, peering curiously at the three strangers carrying her tenant up the stairs.

"No, just terribly drunk," one of the men said, shaking his head sadly. "If he doesn't take better care of himself, booze is going to be the end of him some day."

Once inside, it took only minutes to pump enough gas into Mike to kill him. Then the thugs put everything back in place, tucked Mike into his bed, and left.

In the morning, the men paid off a crooked doctor to pronounce Mike dead from drinking too much. Then, a hasty burial before noon assured the men that no one would have a second chance to look at Mike or question how he died. The thugs were sure that no one would ever discover that they had committed a murder. Mike hadn't had many friends. He was unemployed, and for the past several years he had spent most of his time bumming money for alcohol and then passing out in bars. No one would miss him.

They might have gotten away with their crime if one of the three men had not bragged to a date one evening about how he'd swiped insurance money from an old bum. If he thought that would impress her, he was wrong. She went straight to the police.

Poor old Mike had been buried for three months, but his body was dug up and taken to the hospital for an autopsy. Before the examination even began, both the detectives and the examining doctor suspected carbon monoxide poisoning. It would have been the easiest, quickest, and quietest way to murder a passed-out drunk. In addition, the man who had bragged to his date had said something about "just putting the old bum to sleep."

But would there still be any trace of carbon monoxide in a decomposed body? Doctors had been able to detect high levels of CO in blood a week or more after a body had been discovered in a home or garage, but they doubted that a chemical could linger in a lifeless body after ninety days in the ground. And without proof of carbon monoxide poisoning, the three thugs could not be convicted.

Even the medical examiner was shocked at what he found when he opened Mike up. Both Mike's heart and lungs were still stained a bright cherry red! And though the blood in the corpse had rotted and dried, tests revealed that it still contained an extremely high level of carbon monoxide. There was no doubt about what had happened to Mike. The next week, all three murderers were sentenced to die in the electric chair.

The number of carbon monoxide murders began to decline rapidly after this much-publicized case in the mid-1920s. A new branch of medicine called "forensics" was making things more complicated for murderers. In forensics, doctors studied the human body after death. By putting together the clues, like pieces of a puzzle, doctors could figure out the exact cause of death, when the death occurred, and many other things. Something as obvious as carbon monoxide poisoning was a no-brainer.

As the decades passed, automobile gas became cleaner, and home appliances that used gas became safer. Even so, CO deaths did not disappear. Today, around 170 people in the United States still die each year from carbon monoxide poisoning. Most of these deaths result from misusing appliances that burn gas, oil, coal, or kerosene. All these fuels can emit toxic levels of carbon monoxide when they are burned in poorly ventilated spaces.

Nearly every year, people die while attempting to warm their homes with gas ovens. Using charcoal to cook inside also kills. After Hurricane Katrina, forty-seven people died when they took generators into their houses. The victims' homes did not have enough airflow to flush out the dangerous carbon monoxide that was released from the burning gasoline. And, just like in the 1920s, cars left running in closed garages still claim lives every year.

Today, more and more people are installing carbon monoxide alarms in their homes and workplaces. These alarms work much like smoke detectors do. They beep loudly if they detect too much CO in the air.

"But these alarms only work if you pay attention to them," one health official pointed out. "Too often, people are fooled into thinking there's nothing wrong, since they can't smell or see anything. Plus, they may feel fine, since slow leaks of CO can take weeks or even months to poison a person. But the damage is being done. There's a reason why carbon monoxide is known as the invisible killer."

**If you liked**
***Scary Medical Stories*,**
**you may be interested**
**in other stories**
**in the Townsend Library.**

*continued on the following pages*

Tanya Savory

ANIMAL RESCUE

*A Change of Heart*
*Danelle and Taz*
*Unlikely Heroes*
*The Life Riskers*
*Doctor Fonzie*
*After Hurricane Katrina*
*The Last Hunt*
*Junior*
*A Prince*
*The Orphan Whales*

TP THE TOWNSEND LIBRARY

TEN REAL·LIFE STORIES

The Yellow Ribbon
Shame
Rowing the Bus
The Scholarship Jacket
A Drunken Ride, a Tragic Aftermath
The Professor Is a Dropout
Do It Better
Life Over Death
Becoming a Reader
Learning Survival Skills

TP THE TOWNSEND LIBRARY